THE MICROSCOPIC AND CHEMICAL PARTS OF PLANTS

THE MICROSCOPIC AND CHEMICAL PARTS OF PLANTS

THOMAS P. HANNA

Nova Science Publishers, Inc.
Commack, New York

Editorial Production:	Susan Boriotti
Office Manager:	Annette Hellinger
Graphics:	Frank Grucci and Jennifer Lucas
Information Editor:	Tatiana Shohov
Book Production:	Donna Dennis, Patrick Davin, Christine Mathosian, Tammy Sauter and Lynette Van Helden
Circulation:	Maryanne Schmidt
Marketing/Sales:	Cathy DeGregory

Library of Congress Cataloging-in-Publication Data
available upon request

ISBN 1-56072-547-8

Copyright © 1999 by Nova Science Publishers, Inc.
6080 Jericho Turnpike, Suite 207
Commack, New York 11725
Tele. 516-499-3103   Fax 516-499-3146
e-mail: Novascience@earthlink.net
e-mail: Novascil@aol.com
Web Site: http://www.nexusworld.com/nova

All rights reserved. No part of this book may be reproduced, stored in a retrieval system or transmitted in any form or by any means: electronic, electrostatic, magnetic, tape, mechanical photocopying, recording or otherwise without permission from the publishers.

The authors and publisher have taken care in preparation of this book, but make no expressed or implied warranty of any kind and assume no responsibility for any errors or omissions. No liability is assumed for incidental or consequential damages in connection with or arising out of information contained in this book.

This publication is designed to provide accurate and authoritative information with regard to the subject matter covered herein. It is sold with the clear understanding that the publisher is not engaged in rendering legal or any other professional services. If legal or any other expert assistance is required, the services of a competent person should be sought. FROM A DECLARATION OF PARTICIPANTS JOINTLY ADOPTED BY A COMMITTEE OF THE AMERICAN BAR ASSOCIATION AND A COMMITTEE OF PUBLISHERS.

Printed in the United States of America

Contents

FOREWORD VII

1. AN INTRODUCTION TO ROSE'S BODY 1
2. ROSE IS A PLANT NOT AN ANIMAL 9
3. THIS IS ROSE'S CELL 19
4. THIS IS ROSE'S CELL WALL 27
5. THESE ARE ROSE'S CELL MEMBRANES 37
6. THESE ARE ROSE'S ER AND CYTOSKELETON 47
7. THESE ARE ROSE'S NUCLEUS, CHROMOSOMES AND GENES 55
8. THIS IS BASIC GENETICS IN ROSE 63
9. THESE ARE ROSE'S HYBRIDS 73
10. THESE ARE ROSE'S MITOCHONDRIA 83
11. THESE ARE ROSE'S CHLOROPLASTS 93
12. THESE ARE ROSE'S OTHER CELLULAR "BUBBLES" 103
13. THESE ARE ROSE'S TISSUES 111
14. THIS IS ASEXUAL REPRODUCTION IN ROSE 119
15. THIS IS ROSE'S GROWTH AND DEVELOPMENT 127

16. THESE ARE ABSCISSION AND DEHISCENCE IN ROSE'S BODY 135

17. THESE ARE ROSE'S GROWTH REGULATING CHEMICALS 143

18. THESE ARE ROSE'S PIGMENTS 153

19. THESE ARE ROSE'S SCENTS 161

20. THESE ARE ROSE'S "BEHAVIORS" 171

21. THIS IS ROSE'S TAXONOMIC CLASSIFICATION 179

22. THESE ARE ROSE'S LIFE CYCLES, DORMANCY AND SENESCENCE 189

BIBLIOGRAPHY 197

INDEX 207

FOREWORD

This is a project that I set out to do many years ago and have finally forced myself to sit down and actually put on paper The germ of the idea came from the series of articles on the human body published in *Reader's Digest* between 1967 and 1974 and subsequently put out in book form by Berkley Books. In "I Am Joe's Body" each organ or body system of Joe (or Jane when necessary) described its structure and function in non-technical but useful terms so you got a working appreciation of the body without having to pay for a college prep course. At the time I thought I should do that for the plant body. So I started a filet accumulated notes while I made a living teaching introductory college biology -- and here it is.

For months when I put this topic on the front burner with several other book projects I wrestled with the problem of having the plant parts address the reader directly as Joe's parts had. Two things were particularly problematic about that approach. One was that most of the parts I would need to give voice to occur in numbers, in some cases large numbers, in the single plant so I would be in a constant tap dance between the singular and the plural while trying to describe actions or activities that might occur in each individual unit but would be recognized by casual observers (and thus most readers) as happening in a collective way that would be thought of as singular. The other constant confusion would come from describing what happens in the species *Rosa canina* but wanting or needing to point out the often substantial or numerous differences in other common species since this is intended as a generalized introduction to plant anatomy and function even though focused on the one for emphasis.

Ultimately I had to concede that the danger of misstating myself or confusing the reader was too real if I tried to present the material in the voices of the plant parts themselves. So, being highly adaptable, I shifted the book from *I Am Rose's Body* to *This is Rose's Body* to take advantage of the greater explanatory power of the third person presentation.

Above all else I want this book to hook the reader who thinks he or she cannot understand science because it is "too hard and uses too many strange big words." I hope to pitch a good deal of explanation at the level that most any reasonably intelligent person who makes an effort to pick up the book can understand because my experience from teaching introductory level biology and ecology courses at the college level is that many people are able to be and even want to be captivated by science and will be when they can get into the topics in a non-threatening way. That means the technical terms are defined, the mechanisms are explained using analogies to common experiences, and where necessary we will take two hundred words to spell out the processes step-by-step instead of the highly technical twenty-five words that a scientist would use in explaining it to his peers who speak the jargon in a journal article. They only have time to read so much in a day and expect things to be compact, accepting the fact that this puts the burden on the reader to have the background so that the jargon shorthand is adequate for them.

At first I thought to use *Chrysanthemum leucanthemum*, 'the Ox-eye daisy', as the focus subject since it is a native North American perennial species with a name that fits the bill (This is Daisy's Body) but I decided that a conspicuously woody plant would serve my purpose better because it would stand as the example of all the topics I want to get into, including wood. I chose *Rosa canina*, a true wild species known since pre-Babylonian times (even if it is present in North America since Colonial times as an escapee from cultivation, not a true native) rather than a hybrid form, to sidestep objections about the artificiality or even *unnaturalness* of using a "man-made" type as the model of the plant kingdom. I chose one with single flowers to simplify the discussion of that organ.

This is not a book about roses, it is a book that uses a species of wild rose as a focus example to let me point out some of the features common to the structure and function of many or even most plant species. I hesitated about the choice of species -- and therefore the name for the title -- out of concern that this would be mistaken for another book listing and describing the various botanical and horticultural groups of hybrid roses because the limited but dedicated audience for those books would be disappointed and the much larger group whom I hope to entice to get better acquainted with their photosynthetic neighbors might miss it.

I considered making it the Rose and Lily story to have a Dicot and a Monocot species for comparison but felt that that would obligate me to make major points about the differences in all the chapters and in many the distinctions are not that great. Wherever it seems desirable I do use Lily for comparison but she will not be specifically mentioned in many chapters.

When I had included the basic details of what we have learned in biology in recent decades to make this as complete an introduction as feasible I had so much material that it seemed better to present it in two shorter doses. This volume makes a leap beyond the human body and considers the plant body at the microscopic level, a world of parts only those who have taken a biology course in the last twenty-five years know much about. Our information about these structures and their jobs is being updated regularly but the general pictures I have presented here seem sound for the moment.

Here I also consider major chemical processes of the plant's life (without going into chemical detail) and the tissues, the groups of like cells that form the wallboard, bricks, and shingles used to assemble the organs considered in the other volume of this pair. Many of the things we now know about cells, hormones, and growth and development have close parallels in animals, including ourselves.

This volume is also a suitable place to briefly consider the biological classification system that determines the species we are focusing on is to be called *Rosa canina* by all the biologists in the world and the large amount of information that name (and the unspoken but real parts of the classifying process) tells those in on the game about this form of living thing.

I read and made notes from a great many books over a period of years and that material is condensed here so I cannot give specific credit to most of the sources (although I have gone to some trouble not to quote anyone directly unless I give the appropriate reference).

Writing these chapters took longer than I anticipated because I had to verify all the descriptions and mechanisms I remembered reading about from some recent text or another in order to feel reasonably confident that I am not propagating many claims that are now considered botanical heresy or hopelessly out of date misconceptions. I wanted this to be more than a textbook recitation of body part names so I have allowed myself considerable room to rationalize and theorize about the *whys*, the fairly obvious advantages and disadvantages, of some parts. I accept full responsibility for the errors that may still have slipped in but hope that even they will give some readers the pleasure of refuting them or refining them into conformity with current information.

CHAPTER 1

AN INTRODUCTION TO ROSE'S BODY

Come let us sing the praises of the plants! These green, leafy coinhabitors of our planet are our ancestors and our models in many ways. The first single-celled algae types, the earliest eucaryotic forms that left any fossil evidence, followed the path established by the photosynthetic bacteria and the blue-green algae (now called *Cyanobacteria)* that predated them and helped to lay the foundations which would allow animals to evolve.

The plants are the original inventors and the list of their accomplishments is long and glorious. They are engineering wonders and they have done the engineering themselves. They invented the compartmentalized eucaryotic cell, and later cooperation and specialization in multicellularity. They were the first and remain the only eucaryotes to develop the food-making capacity by photosynthesis. They invented swimming among eucaryotes -- a skill which some single celled algae types still practice. They invented sex -- for which we will be eternally grateful to them -- since sexual reproduction produces genetic variability in any population and that both eliminates monotony and increases the likelihood of survival of the species when there are changes in the local environment. (What did you think I meant?) They helped produce a twenty percent oxygen atmosphere, invented recycling to reuse the mineral nutrients from their own discarded body parts, and even invented death as an escape when we have done our part (since the bacteria types theoretically rejuvenate themselves by dividing into two "young" cells so the specific gene combinations never need to cease "because of old age" the way all multicellular life forms do).

The plants invented flying buttresses, guy wires, parachutes, pipe systems, corrugation for strength with minimum weight, and stilts to rise above floodwaters. They developed fly paper, antibiologicals to fight various disease-causing microbes, chemical pesticides (still the only reasonably safe ones, like rotenone), hormones, biological clocks, calendars, and perfume.

Not only have plants as a group been around much longer than we have but some individual plants have been alive and growing continuously for much longer than any of us can imagine living. We know that some bristlecone pines and giant *Sequoia* trees in California are at least 4000 years old.

Plants are still the dominant species in almost every biological community. They establish the local environment by altering the existing conditions and all other species must adapt to these modified conditions, move out, or die. In essentially every community the number and kinds of plants that are available as food are a prime determinant of what animal species can survive there. Ultimately they control all other species including us in the sense that we literally cannot live without them in the form of the various products we derive from them. They provide our food (90 percent of our calories and 80 percent of our protein intake, on a worldwide average), much of our oxygen, our- building material, and our other day-to-day material needs, plus the pacification that we often need from the tensions of daily life. It is not an accident that green is psychologically the most relaxing of colors.

Plants are living things with essentially all of the basic biochemical functions of the animals since they developed from the same ancestral one-celled types. Plants and animals perform most of the same life functions, they just do some in slightly different ways. Within the limits of any particular function the plants as a group have probably tried every conceivable variation or modification (and some that not even the most imaginative scientist would have suggested) of the ways of doing the biological jobs. The very extent of the variations in everything makes it difficult to talk about *plants* as a common group. The specific types are very much individuals.

There are major areas of difference though. Plants share with a group of microbe types the role of being both primary synthesizers of organic compounds and selective accumulators of inorganic nutrients from the soil and water. All animals, fungi and the other microbes must derive most of the organic and even many of the inorganic molecules they need from their food.

Plants share the planet with us and share life with us but we often find it hard to really think of them as living because they are different in some major ways from ourselves. The plants live and function on different time and distance scales that those used by animals which is part of the reason that we tend to think of them as being insensitive, unresponsive, unchanging things just sitting there vegetating. When observed from the right vantage point the plants will be found to sway, shiver, and maybe even flush with excitement. They grow, respond, and move (although seldom from place to place as intact, mature plants in a short time frame) but do it so slowly or "close in" that we only notice when we watch very carefully. Like everything else about plants as the large group, there are exceptions. Some of the large bamboos -- grasses that grow eighty feet tall -- grow so fast they can add a foot of new shoot in a day. And they may make a lot of noise doing it as the rapidly lengthening shoot breaks through restricting stem coverings in the process.

We tend to think of life in animal terms. We associate it with breathing, rapid movement, complex behaviors, and probably some exchange of signs of awareness of us, and possibly even interest in or affection for us. Plants do not do these things in ways that we recognize so we tend to think of them as parts of the background but not really alive even though we recognize that they have what we technically define as life because they grow, reproduce, and die (often in spite of our best intentioned efforts to take care of them). They may seem more like some kind of E.T.'s, friendly and perhaps decorative but still foreign and unknown. You look at a dog or a canary or a cow and think *alive*, but do you have the same awareness that you are considering a living being when you look at a tomato, a banana, or an oak tree?

From the Hanging Gardens of Babylon, one of the wonders of the Ancient World, to the straggly geranium over-wintering on the windowsill of some back country cottage, plants have always been with us and important to us. In part this involves the simple essentials for survival; in part it is a matter of choice because we enjoy having them around us. In recent years this interest has taken one of its periodic upturns. Plants have become very "in" as decorations, hobby items, and green companions. Not to have at least a few live plants around is considered by some to be roughly the equivalent of not having chairs for your guests to sit on. Today we spend a considerable amount of time and effort fussing over, talking about, and talking to our plants (or talking about those who talk too openly to their plants). Yet far too many people have no more idea of what makes their favorite philodendron grow than they do about how a computer computes or an internal combustion engine combusts.

This book is intended to fill that gap. This is not a book about how to grow plants, but rather one about how plants grow. It is an invitation to get inside your plants and understand why you do for them all the things that the how-to-grow-them books recommend.

Immediately many people will be inclined to throw up their hands and protest, "I'm not a biologist. I cannot understand all of that technical stuff." There is no doubt that a major part of the difficulty of learning any specialized topic is the technical terminology. For those working in the field this is verbal shorthand and the methodology of expressing very precise and possibly complicated concepts in as few words as possible. The non-professional normally does not need the highest degree of precision in dealing with the topics, nor does he or she have the awareness of the historical development of the theories and information that that technical terminology reflects and somewhat justifies. But certainly if you are going to talk about the more conspicuous parts and activities of any system -- whether a living plant, a manufacturing process, a diesel engine, or some sport -- you need to learn a few new terms and how they are applied. Then you can get by, both understanding what is happening and being able to discuss it intelligently and intelligibly with other people who also understand the basics of the system. When you understand the Latin and Greek roots from which the biological words are formed, you will see that the terms are very descriptive. As often as possible I will emphasize these root meanings when I introduce new terms.

We are all aware that words have shade or "color" of meaning. There may be several words that denote basically the same thing but each has its own overtones. Minivans, jalopies, convertibles, and limousines are all "automobiles" but precisely which type a man is driving will tend to suggest different things to others about his financial, professional, and even personal position and attitudes and will probably affect his self-perception as well. In a comparable way umbels, panicles, corymbs, and racemes are all terms for the arrangement of individual flowers on the full stems of different plant groups but they are not interchangeable. These terms immediately tell a botanist what shape the overall flower head will be and whether all the flowers will be open simultaneously. The terms narrow the number of plant families an unseen but described plant can belong to, additional information supplied to the prepared person without needing to add a syllable to the description.

None of the basic biology of botany gets too technical for any person of ordinary intelligence to grasp as long as it is presented in the right way. The advantage we will make full use of in this book is that I do not have to describe the basic botanical structures and functions in the minimum number of words and I can skip the little details when they are not necessary to understanding the basic workings of the parts. This book is written precisely to explain the basics and I can spell it out in bits and pieces, taking space to use some comparisons that I think might be helpful. We will not enter into most of the highly technical and specialized areas so we will not concern ourselves about all the precise details, most of the chemistry, any of the mathematical analyses, and therefore the most complicated terminology. You will learn about these if you are inclined to pursue the topics because your instructors in courses or textbooks will be people who know those areas well.

In this book I want to wet your feet in the terminology in order to whet your intellectual appetite in such a way that you will find the immersion not only painless but positively interesting, stimulating, and fun. You will be surprised at how quickly and easily you will be using the "fancy words" naturally, accurately, and unself-consciously.

In recent years animals have become better known and appreciated by large numbers of people because they have been the subject of a variety of television *Wildlife* programs. I am all in favor of this type of program as a form of entertainment and as a mode of education. I attempt to see them all. Through this medium many people who had never heard of an aardvark except as a tricky item beginning with a double *a* in a crossword puzzle now know what one looks like, how it goes about making its living as a termite eater, and maybe even why it has a white tail. (For those readers who did not see that particular PBS *Nature* program the answer is that the young animal follows its mother as she hurries through the night by keeping track of that bit of white.)

Little of the attention in these programs, however, has been devoted to plants, except in a general "there are plants all around that form the forest in which these fascinating little animals creep, crawl, and meander" way. I hope to see this change because I am convinced that plants, properly presented, are fully as fascinating in their ways as the animals. I recognize that there is a preconception by TV producers and programmers that plants are not as effective as subjects because they do not run around, wink at the camera, beg for handouts, or allow themselves to be "captured on film for the first time ever while. . ." For the intellectually curious, however, they have many fascinations. The series of programs by David Attenborough first aired in 1995 is a move to fill this deficiency that has gotten high praise and such endeavors are to be encouraged.

We should begin our consideration of botany by asking a question which will make it obvious that scientific knowledge is not as complete or as absolute as many people believe. In fact some of the most basic questions are the ones for which we do not have good answers although we may be able to answer very surely and with elaborate detail some of the more specific inquiries.

The very basic question is, *What is a plant?* The interesting fact is that we cannot give a completely satisfactory answer. We can list some generalizations which hold for the majority of cases and argue that, while no single criterion we have yet recognized will hold up to careful scrutiny as the definitive identifying trait because there are always exceptions and gray areas, the combination of the features noted is a reasonably good definition. **More about this in Chapter 2.** This, in fact, seems to be a characteristic of many of the seemingly fundamental questions in science and some other areas of human concern. What is energy? What is life? What is God? What is good? Or just? Or moral? Universally agreed upon absolute definitions are hard to come by but widely accepted working definitions are available.

I have selected Rose as a typical seed plant that happens to have a common and botanical name conducive to my purpose of attracting your-attention. She is very different from many members of the plant kingdom, even from many of the other species around the world with "rose" in their common but not their botanical names, but she has more in common with the other multicellular plant species than she does with the multicellular animal types of the world. Similarities and differences are the basic data of the natural world. They allow us to sort, categorize, and catalog the rich variety of living types and their ancestors identifiable in the fossil record. It is precisely on the basis of similarities that we call one group of living organisms plants to distinguish them from another large group that have many features that are similar and that we call the animals. Rose is a woody perennial plant which gives me license to consider the features of wood tissue and the important topics of dormancy and abscission as well as senescence.

An initial problem with a description of the plant body is that there are so many known species (more than 330,000 by some counts) and therefore so much variation. And here already in this estimated number an item on which there is not universal agreement among the professionals. The temptation is very strong to point out and describe many of the common variance patterns but I have tried to limit myself to describing the features as seen in the chosen examples of the roses since this is a special introduction to the plant, not a standard botany textbook (where you can find all those other forms and variations described and where I would be delighted if you were intrigued enough to go and seek out that information). For many of the topics I have taken a bit of liberty in that I describe the common structures and functions that have been described as probably common to most woody dicot species without making specific claim that they are exactly so in *Rosa canina*.

A caution. There are exceptions to almost everything one can say about living things so none of my statements should be taken as absolutes although I have tried to stick to topics and observations that are well recognized and analyzed.

A distinction that is fundamental to flowering plant classification is that between Dicots, species like Rose that have two cotyledons or "seed leaves" on the seedling and a list of other common features like long stems with relatively few leaves, and Monocots like Lily, those with a single cotyledon and a list of different features like long thin leaves and little stem. There will be more about this in **Chapter 21**. At a few points it will be useful to point out consistent differences between the structures of the two groups and there Lily will stand in as a reasonably typical Monocot species.

Rosa canina, the "Dog rose" or "Briar rose" is the most common wild rose native to Britain and Europe. It was introduced even there from its true Mediterranean home by the Romans but became so widespread it was often assumed to have developed there naturally. In the same way it became naturalized in eastern North American shortly after European settlers arrived here and planted it in their gardens. It is today a standard wild, if not native, species in North America.

R. canina inermis, a thornless or unarmed variety introduced into cultivation by M. Gamon of Lyon, France about 1905 is the most popular rose understock in Canada and Europe. As of 1981 it was considered the best canina variety to bud or graft hybrid teas, floriburidas, and climbers. There are at least 60 varieties or forms of the species that are recognized in or out of horticulture.

The common name dog *rose* presents an interesting problem. It may have come from some resemblance of the many curved prickles to a dog's tooth or from a belief that the root could cure the bite of a mad dog. The Romans carried the plant to England because they believed it had medicinal value, not primarily as an ornamental. Sixteenth century sources recommended roses and wine for a hangover and advised that roses could be used for eye strain, sore throats, bad gums, weak heart, melancholia, rashes, eczema, ringworm, and liver and kidney problems. Early American settlers also thought roses the cure for almost every malady which may explain why early on they introduced *R. canina*, a species they would have confidence in from home.

The name rose comes from the Celtic word for red, processed through the Latin and Greek. These flowers have become symbols of love, virtue, trust, virginity, secrecy, and the fall of man. The rose was chosen of the emblem of many countries, towns, and families over the centuries. They are also sources of wines, dyes, medicines, perfumes, pomanders, and potpourris.

In the Ancient world the rose was the symbol of Aphrodite. It was also sacred to Venus, the goddess of love. In this context its thorns were said to represent the pain that love can inflict while its beauty and fragrance reminded one of the perfection of love. Later in Europe it came to be associated with the Virgin Mary as Christianity absorbed and modified some of the mythical symbols.

A Greek legend relates that Chloris, the goddess of flowers, found a dead nymph and asked the other gods to transmute her into a special flower. Aphrodite gave the new flower beauty, the Graces gave brilliance, Apollo provided breezes to waft her perfume, and Dionysius, the god of wine, gave her nectar. Thus was the Rose formed. Cupid then gave the new flower to Harpocrates, the god of silence. From this we get the expression *sub rosa* or "under- the rose" to indicate something that is to be kept secret. Until at least the Seventeenth century a rose was hung from the ceiling of a room in which secrecy and silence were to be observed. Still today ceiling paintings in many council chambers often include the rose motif as a tradition although the meaning has been largely forgotten.

The oldest known or suspected living plant of *R. Canina* I thought to be at the garden of Hildesheim, planted by a son of Charlemagne about 820 A.D.

CHAPTER 2

ROSE IS A PLANT NOT AN ANIMAL

Almost no one old enough to walk and talk would have a serious problem designating Rose as a plant rather than an animal even if he had no idea what kind of plant she might be. Very few of those who know she is a plant, however, could give a detailed explanation of why that is the case. You learn early to distinguish the broad categories of animal versus vegetable versus mineral but seldom because you are taught specific rules for identifying each. It is like learning the difference between your stuffed teddy bear and the family puppy. You pick up hints here and there and build a poorly examined set of criteria based mostly on matching your classification with those of family and friends who are older and presumably wiser or at least more experienced in these things, plus a few observations of your own about feel and responsiveness.

Biologists, who adopted the ages old flora or fauna distinction as technical terms did so to have a shorthand for telling one another a lot about a new living species in a word or two. They used a group of specific characteristics to distinguish plant and animals on the basis of similarities and differences, the foundation of all the sorting and grouping activities that we as a species seem compelled to do. Some of these traits are features of each of the many individual cells that make up a multicellular organism's body but some are features of the organism, the group of cells functioning as a unit. The vexing problem of whether a single-celled species is plant or animal is today sidestepped by the Biologists by simply designating additional kingdoms in the classification system to contain those. Since people constructed the system they can make alterations to improve or correct it whenever it seems warranted.

To simplify this topic a bit I will focus on the flowering plants as *plants* and the insects and vertebrates as *animals* since they are the most evolved groups in their categories and the types most non-biologists are most familiar with. Some of the distinctions become less clear when we look at the simpler or "lower" (on the, evolutionary ladder) plant and animal forms.

Plants and animals and even the single-celled critters are fundamentally alike in that all are made of protoplasm organized into cells and are alive, those two conditions being close to identical. Protoplasm varies enormously in exact chemical composition between life forms but it is characterized by having a high degree of organization with most of its mass composed of four classes of macromolecules that are assembled by hooking together into chains a relatively small number of kinds of interchangeable small building block molecule types to form a very large number of different complex polymer-molecules with specific and critical three-dimensional shapes. These classes are the proteins, nucleic acids, lipids, and carbohydrates.

All living things are alike in having the physiological processes of *respiration* in which they release energy from molecular bonds for use in maintaining the cell, *assimilation* in which they convert chemical materials from outside into new protoplasm, and *irritability* that is the capacity to detect and respond to changes in their internal and/or external environment.

The plants differ from the animals very conspicuously in their mode of nutrition. Plants form their own food or storable energy-rich molecules so they are *autotrophs* or "self-feeders" but animals must obtain and digest energy-rich molecules that have been formed by other species (ultimately the plants) so they are *heterotrophs* or "other feeders".

There are three features of plant cells that are notably unlike those of animals that we will consider in some detail in later- chapters. Plant cells have cell walls (**Chapter 4**), many contain chloroplasts or other chromoplasts (**Chapter 11**), and the mature cells typically have a large central vacuole (**Chapter 12**). Here we will briefly consider two other cell differences.

It is a routine part of the development of many animal embryos to have groups of cells formed by mitotic cell divisions in one spot then literally move themselves into another area to form parts of the tissue they are programmed to be. This is particularly noticeable with neurons in the central nervous system and some types of white blood cell precursors. Nothing like this has been reported in plant growth areas.

Programmed cell death or *apoptosis* is also a feature of animal embryonic development and some later functioning in their tissues. Masses of cells form and then some of them selectively commit suicide using built-in genetic means. They die and leave the other cells positioned and ready to function in the finished animal. Plants also have selective cell death, most notably in their xylem cells but here the call wall usually remains in place and continues to function while in animals the dead cells are cleared out and leave no trace. Except for the xylem cells, the plant cells that die after a period of use do so because new cells forming deeper in the root or stem either crush them (as happens in the secondary phloem) or push them so far from the food and water supply lines that they starve (as happens to cork cells of the bark) rather than committing suicide from within themselves -- although a self-inflicted *coup de grace* probably cannot be absolutely ruled out.

In most animal cells a pair of centrioles (bundles of nine protein rods laid in parallel, with the, bundles at right angles to one another) are found near the nucleus most of the time. These play an important role during any cell division. They are not found in the flowering plants, however. Here a temporary structure referred to as the *spindle* because of its shape forms early in the cell division process and disappears again after doing the same job as the centrioles when the separation of the chromosome copies is completed. Also in the late stages of a cell division an animal cell forms a furrow or constriction at the midline that pinches in until it separates the cytoplasm into two parts. In plant cells there is no furrowing, instead a new *cell plate* -forms across the midline of the original cell which becomes the middle lamella between the two new cells when it is complete and they rapidly form new cell walls on either side of it.

There are several features of Rose as a total organism that are notably different from what we find in most animals, starting with her growth pattern which is quite typical of plants.

Most increase in size of any multicellular organism results from an increase in the number of its cells. This increase results from cell division by the process called mitosis. The resulting cells then *differentiate* or emphasize certain structures and possibly lose others in order to be most efficient at specific jobs within the body. In the process they also increase in size as they rapidly synthesize new proteins and other needed molecule types. In plant cells much of the increase in size is the result of water filling them and forming the central bubble or vacuole that may occupy more than seventy percent of the cell's volume. Animal cells increase in size by packing themselves with new protoplasm and relatively less water and especially not a large water-filled bubble.

Within limits Rose will grow throughout her entire life, getting larger every season unless something happens to restrain her. Rose's individual stems will not grow indefinitely but she will produce more stems as she ages, some to replace ones that have died or been removed by animals, storms, or disease and some simply reflecting the fact that she is healthy and has enough food reserves to allow her to expand herself to do more photosynthesis and to make more flowers to multiply the number of her offspring. Animals, with a few exceptions like crocodiles, grow to their maximum size relatively early in their lives and stay that size for the rest of their years. Some plant species or varieties do have a similar limited growth pattern. *Determinate* varieties of tomato that produce one batch of fruit that all ripen at the same time are a common example. The *indeterminate* varieties are the ones that set new fruit from July until frost. It is not an accident that the largest creatures that ever lived (that we know about) are the Giant Sequoia trees in California. They have been growing slowly but relentlessly, adding a bit to their height and their girth each year for more than 4000 years.

Most non-tropical plants have an active growing phase followed by a dormant period during unfavorable weather. They produce a certain amount of growth for the season and then stop. If they lose leaves or branches to insects or other damage they may replace those even beyond the normal growth period. The next season they are back at it though, adding another increment of length to their stems and replacing all or some of the leaves of the previous season. In tropical areas some species grow all year round. Animal breeding and the consequent rapid growth of the new young is often tied to the seasonal changes in the availability of food but animal growth does not show a comparable on-off with the seasons pattern if the food supply is adequate.

In Rose the new growth beyond her first season as a seedling is supported by her woody tissue in the sense that the new growth is initially non-woody and grows from buds produced along the older woody stem sections. This new growth each year is where she produces her leaves and flowers. The old woody stems serve to position the new growth for the best exposure to sunlight and pollination. Many plant species "migrate" to a better position by extending their stems in the desired direction over several seasons while the roots remain fixed in the original spot. Thus a seed that sprouted back under a shrub "crawls out" to where it can hold its leaves beyond the shade of the shrub or pushes its stems up through those of the shrub and lets those branches support most of the weight while the underling sticks its leaves out between those of the shrub. For such "crawlers" the migration may also involve forming new adventitious roots along the stems that are lying on the ground so that when it gets its leaves into the sun the roots are nearby even though it sprouted as much as several feet away. Rose plants might be found that have traveled either of these routes.

This also illustrates why plants go to some trouble to get the wind or animals to help them spread their seeds around. If all the seeds fall beside and beneath the parent they have to compete with it for light, soil, moisture, and space. Gardeners note that many of the perennial species they cultivate follow a pattern of growing new stems on the edges of the clumps each year so that over time the clump gets wider but the center dies out. The result is that the species are migrating in slow motion around the beds and they must be repositioned periodically or the intended garden design gets obscured.

By producing new foliage and flowers at the end of woody stems a plant like Rose can increase the number of new stems and thus the amount of photosynthetic food production and the number of flowers it can make without having the leaves all in a stack where they would shade one another and reduce their efficiency. Using woody stems as the framework lets the plant position the chlorophyll-containing leaf tissues over a wide area to get unshaded light without interfering with any essential functions of those stems. When the water supply is minimal non-woody stems might not have the strength to hold the leaves and flowers in position.

Another aspect of Rose's growth pattern that distinguishes her from an animal is that the increase in the number of her cells is limited to a few localized tissues called *meristems* that are located mainly at the tip of each shoot and root to let those lengthen. An additional thin layer wraps around the shoots and roots so they can increase in diameter.

At the base of each leaf Rose retains a small bit of meristem tissue that forms a dormant *axillary bud*. If something destroys the stem farther out from the roots this bud can be activated to grow into a replacement branch. If by the next growing season the intact stem beyond that bud is still in good shape this bud may become active and form an additional branch extending out in a different direction. As long as the terminal or tip bud is growing properly it would be inefficient to have too much foliage in one tight spot where it would shade itself so the axial buds stay dormant as a backup that requires a minimum of maintenance. Animals have nothing comparable to these buds.

The position of the meristems means that plant growth is limited to lengthening of shoots and roots with a minimal increase in diameter in any short period. When they are growing, animals tend to be increasing in size all over in a less constrained way because they do not depend on such localized tissues to carry out cell division.

Animals can grow a limited number of any kind of major organ. One liver, two kidneys, three small bones in each inner ear. That is all their genetic program will allow. And no replacements for those later although they may be able to repair them to some degree. By contrast most plants can produce an indefinite number of leaves or stems or flowers over a lifetime, each as functional as any other of their type.

Once beyond the earliest embryonic stages animals have limited powers of regeneration for whole organs or body parts. If a man loses an arm he will have to make do with an artificial one. If a tree loses all the branches from a major limb it can grow new ones to replace them as a matter of routine. If we take that severed arm and keep it clean and well watered it will not grow into a new man (except in certain science fiction stories of course). Given the right conditions even in Nature some of the pieces broken off a tree or bush in a storm may end up with the stem partly buried in the soil where they can indeed grow into whole new trees. Plants are said to have *totipotency*, the capacity to grow all of the body parts from the specialized or differentiated mature tissues of some body areas. Although some animals like salamanders may grow a whole new leg if one is amputated, animals do not have totipotency except these days in a somewhat different sense when we manipulate egg cells of a few species in the laboratory to produce cloned frogs and turkeys.

Animals perform many specialized tasks only within special localized organs like a liver, a small intestine, or a brain. Most plants do not have any essential functions that are so localized. You can remove a large part of the stem or many of the roots or shoot branches of most plant species without stopping any particular function because the jobs are more spread out and are performed by many less specialized cells rather than by a few highly dedicated ones. The major exception is sexual reproduction which is restricted to specific organs in both plants and animals but even here there is the difference that an animal produces sexual reproduction cells only in its one pair of gonads (ovaries or testes) but a plant like Rose produces them in every flower on every branch and brand new ones each year.

We can make the generalization that plants are immobile and passive while animals tend to be mobile and active. This is a direct consequence of the fact that the plants have explored another path in the world of possibilities open to living things. Early on they made a major choice which accounts for a great many of the differences between them and animals when they developed semi-rigid cell walls to surround and protect their cells. Although it sacrifices most motility this modification allows them to compete better among themselves for vital sunlight exposure by growing upright, even to great heights. And they can maintain this upright posture holding the leaves and flowers in position for long periods without getting tired.

Being rooted in place works for plants because their big need is to hold parts in space and in the sun with little need to move them around and the negative effect of self-shading if they do. Also both soil and air space are limiting factors for them so once a plant has established itself it would be risky to move since there is no way it can be assured of finding another, much less a better, spot elsewhere and the current one may not be vacant if it has to give up that search. This ties in with its need to absorb water more or less continuously and to get most of the minerals it needs dissolved in that water. Water in the air is not as reliable a resource as what is being held in place by capillarity and other forces in the soil and what is in the air will have significantly less dissolved mineral material. A foothold in the soil is a big advantage considering the plant's needs. Staying in place also allows them to recycle minerals from their own discarded parts that are composted right there at the base of the plant by microbes. If the plant moves on it cannot take that resource with it.

Being fixed in place does require that plants develop methods to disperse their offspring, both to spread them out locally and to send some exploring into more distant areas. Young animals routinely migrate out of the local population to keep it from becoming overcrowded but plants must do that while they are embryos in seeds with no control over where they end up.

The rigidity of plant parts limits most local scale movements so it would have served no purpose for them to evolve elaborate sensory systems and behaviors. As we will note in **Chapter 17** they have mostly growth responses to stimuli, not songs, bites, or ducking for cover.

The design of plants also allows them to more readily shed unnecessary or damaged body parts. This is a plant characteristic that we find little in animals to compare with. A plant that shades its own lower leaves too much as it grows will drop the lower ones without great trauma. Animals regularly shed hair, feathers, or individual layers of skin cells (all dead cells for all or most of their functional existence we might note) but not whole functional organs. A lizard may give up a tail or an insect a leg to escape from a predator but these are emergency measures and only a few members of the species every have to utilize them. Plants regularly and routinely shed major body parts as a normal part of their growth.

Coupled with this is the ability to produce new body parts repeatedly. A deciduous plant sheds its leaves every year during the cold or the dry season and just as predictably grows a whole new set when the environmental conditions warrant. A mammal grows a new fur coat each year and a bird one or two changes of plumage but they don't grow a new digestive system or new wings and feet.

Except in some tropical areas it is normal for plants to spend a part of each year in a dormant state because they cannot efficiently carry out their many activities when it is too cold, too hot or, in the high latitudes, too dark (which is often a combination of light quality and day length). Relatively few animal types go into a state approximating plant dormancy, true hibernators and estivators being the main exceptions. Most animals spend the "off season" still needing to feed and grow even if at a slower rate (as would be the case in those types that do not maintain a constant body temperature).

The presence of a cell wall that must be reinforced by turgor or water pressure makes plant cells and non-woody plant body parts more dependent on control of osmosis than is obvious in animal cells. This is reflected in the fact that carbohydrates, especially sugars and polysaccharides, are found in greater quantity and variety in plant cells because by switching them from sugars to starch and back the cell can readily affect its osmotic condition or water balance. Starches are common components in plant cells but seldom found in animals where a different polysaccharide, glycogen, performs the major task of medium term storage.

Plants protect themselves from some fungi and animals but actively seek to attract others, which reflects long-term evolutionary adaptations that usually are mutual accommodations between some beneficial species and the plant host or provider. There are many more beneficial fungus-plant interactions than fungus-animal ones but this is a general trait they share with animals rather than a difference.

Sexual reproduction requires that there be a way to keep the number of chromosomes in the cells from doubling every generation and that way is to have most species be diploid or *2n* organisms with two complete sets of the genes of the species (= n) in equivalent or homologous pairs. A cell division process called meiosis separates special cells into haploid or *n* cells that subsequently act as the reproductive cells (sperm and eggs) and can fuse in fertilization to form new diploid individuals. Plants and animals have sexual reproduction and the overall processes are the same but the details have major differences, especially that in the plants the haploid forms become multicellular entities that have a brief semi-independent existence but in animals they remain single cells.

In addition, plants regularly are found to have three or more complete sets of the genes of the species so they are *polyploids*, a condition found only in a very few animal species. For unexplained reasons in most animals having extra DNA in the cells produces severe harmful effects like mental retardation or early death, usually during the embryonic stages, but we see no such harmful effects in the plants. Polyploidy even gives plants an additional way to form new species that animals cannot utilize since an individual with an odd number of sets of chromosomes is almost always sterile which is an evolutionary deadend. If one plant of a diploid or 2n species has a genetic accident that causes its chromosomes not to divide when the cell division cycle begins it may survive intact but it will now have double the number of chromosomes (4n) of its original species. If it subsequently divides normally that pattern becomes fixed in it. But now if it mates with a plant of the original species all the resulting offspring will be triploid (2n + n = 3n) and sterile but if it pollinates itself the offspring are fertile (2n + 2n = 4n) polyploids like itself. In this case then a new species, one able to produce fertile offspring only with others of its own kind, can form in a single growing season.

It is also possible to produce *graft hybrids*, individual plants containing parts cut from two or more different plants and positioned so they grow together and from then on grow as one plant although they are not a new species since they must be produced by us and still produce the pollen and eggs of whichever species were used for the top growth. In this way we get dwarfed, disease resistant fruit trees with sections of three different types in their stems and trees that produce five types of apples on separate branches.

Chapter 3

This is Rose's Cell

To fully understand any living thing we must be able to describe its structure, its functions, and its development in detail. And to do that we must begin with the individual cell. Here we will take a careful look at these marvelous microscopic units of life in Rose as a representative flowering plant.

All cells are formed on a basic pattern and are probably more alike than they are different. In this chapter we will consider some features that they have in common and see what features allow the great amount of diversity within the common patterns. We will consider the major cellular parts in some detail in **chapters 4 through 7 and 10 through 12.**

The wisdom and experience of many biologists has been condensed into a series of three statements that form the Modern Cell Theory, the basis of our concepts of biology for the last 150 years. First, all living things are composed of cells. Having a cellular structure is in fact the closest thing we have to a good and official definition of being a lifeform -- although the particular unit could be dead and still have its cellular structure intact so the definition is not absolute. Anything that does not have this degree of organization is suspect and subject to qualifications when we ask if it is alive. Viruses are the main inhabitants of this gray zone. They are too numerous, diverse, and biologically important to be ignored but they do not perform most of the functions we commonly expect of living things and they must commandeer a living cell to reproduce, the main thing that they do that makes them seem somewhat alive.

Second, under existing environmental conditions all cells come from previously existing cells. In the early stages of the earth before there was a high oxygen atmosphere -- which developed because of photosynthetic bacteria and then the early plants -- it probably was possible for life to got started from the "primeval soup" of less organized chemicals that formed in the warm shallow seas or in the mud but that time has passed with those atmospheric conditions. We believe that spontaneous generation, non-living material suddenly turning into something alive, is no longer possible in the world today (except in Sci Fi or horror movies, of course).

Third, cells are the basic units of structure and function of all living things. This is extremely important because it focuses our attention immediately on the cell as a critical level to be examined closely to understand how plants, and all living things, do the things they do.

Cells are difficult to make workable analogies about because they do things so differently from most of our man-made systems. Each is a building, a manufacturing unit, and the end product all in one. The component cells of a multicellular plant are like the inhabitants of a kingdom busily doing all the jobs that need doing to make the whole kingdom survive, with most of the workers being highly specialized.

Bigger is prettier because at the cellular level most things look much alike. It is the beauty of well designed and functioning systems that is the big draw of the cell.

Our understanding of cells has been directly tied to our technological methods and equipment. As we developed better microscopes and methods of staining and chemically treating specimens to get more visible contrast between different cell types and cell parts we have learned more about how they are put together and how they work.

In the 1930s we developed the first electron microscopes. These can give us magnifications up to 100,000X. Suddenly vastly more detail than was invisible with even the best light microscope (that could magnify a maximum of 2000X) came sweeping into focus before an electron beam and a cathode-ray tube, Perhaps the biggest surprise when we were able to view their interiors in enough details to see cell membranes in cross section was the high degree of organization in cells. With only the light microscope views to go on it had been assumed that a cell was pretty much a bag of jelly-like protoplasm with things almost randomly arranged and possibly able to shift around somewhat. The reality is that in all cells except the bacteria the contents are compartmentalized by membranes into a group of specialized structures that are devoted to particular tasks and are shaped to do them most efficiently. These *organelles* or "little organs", some of which we did not even suspect existed until then, are literal evidence that in a cell there is a place for everything and for the cell to continue to function everything must be in its place.

A great deal of work in cellular chemistry in the 1950's correlated specific functions with the newly discovered organelles so that we made quantum leaps forward in our knowledge and understanding. Cells provide those delightful surprises usually reserved to Chinese boxes where each one opens to reveal another, smaller, closed box within. In the cell these neatly packaged surprises are the vast expanses of surfaces fitted within a minimal volume. Engineering marvels at every turn.

Here under the student light microscope was the little grass-green oval of a chloroplast in a leaf cell, just one of dozens of small green dots visibly moving with the tide of protoplasmic streaming in a dignified parade around the cell's interior. But seen in cross-section with the electron 'scope it is layer upon layer, stack upon stack, of carefully placed and precisely spaced membrane working units for photosynthesis. What a marvel to realize that because of this packing design a mature oak tree has in its leaves some 150 square miles of surface for trapping solar light energy for photosynthesis.

It took further improvements in our specimen staining techniques using antibodies as research tools for us to finally see what we were missing even with the electron 'scope, the presence of a skeleton of thin protein tubes and rods that extends throughout the cell and helps maintain its three dimensional shape, helps many animal cell types to move, and provides a framework along which materials can be moved from place to place within the cell in a controlled way. There is still some general purpose cytoplasm with no known specific function filling in the spaces but there is a lot less in a cell that does not seem to have assigned tasks than we used to think.

Genes and the environment interact to shape any living thing so we need to recognize some basic facts. First, the cells of each different kind of organism in the world are different in some genetic-based ways from those of any and every other kind of living thing. Every species is unique.

Second, the cells of different members of the same species differ in some ways from one another. These are the individual differences. Many are based on genes, some are dependent on gender, and some are the result of the specific environmental conditions during the development of this individual organism.

Third, the cells within any multicellular organism may differ from one another in some structural and therefore functional ways. This is what allows them to be specialized for specific tasks.

Fourth, any particular cell may change in some or many ways during its lifetime. Each cell has multiple identities. It is relatively self-contained while also a functional member of a tissue, and of some particular body part or organ, and thereby of the overall multicellular plant.

Each cell is a small package of *protoplasm* (from the Greek, "first form"). It is a mass of chemicals wrapped in membrane bags. This protoplasm has highly organized parts composed mostly of organic molecules whose major purpose is to maintain and, given the chance, multiply the cell. This is a far more difficult job than a non-living thing faces because the living material must carry on a lot of specific, energy-requiring chemical reactions just to keep itself unchanged from minute to minute. It must preserve an internal chemical environment that is highly organized and significantly different in specific ways from its non-living surroundings.

This means it must have tools and these are mostly the group of protein molecule types that we call enzymes. The instructions for making these are stored in the genes so they can be made inside the cell whenever it needs that particular tool but they do not need to be kept around at other times. This is critically important because it is hard for a cell to have an enzyme present but keep it from reacting even when that is not desirable or would even be dangerous. The easy solution is to destroy all enzymes not needed that very moment and remake them only as they are needed, reusing the amino acids to make other proteins.

Part of the difference from the non-living parts of the world is that cells use only about thirty of the 92 naturally occurring chemical elements in their cells and these are often in very different proportions than they are usually found in any nonliving materials. In fact only four of the elements (carbon, hydrogen, oxygen and nitrogen) make up 95 percent by weight of typical protoplasm. Add in calcium and magnesium and we have accounted for 99 percent of the weight.

As living entities, cells are constantly changing. They are taking in chemical raw materials and energy in the form of light or energy-containing molecules, and they are giving off other chemicals and energy, usually in the form of heat, just as continuously. All the intermediate chemical steps in which the incoming energy and molecules are being utilized in an orderly way to produce the essential materials for the living, growing, self-repairing cell occur within the cells or as a direct result of materials released by them into their immediate surroundings. The unusable or poisonous by-products are released to the outside as waste chemicals and unusable heat energy. In the process the cells are, in a broad sense, continuing the process of organic evolution because they are taking in inorganic materials and incorporating them into the complex organic molecule types of their own living systems. These molecule types are unmistakably the products of cells. Being able to make such complex molecules using energy coming originally from the sun or the mineral part of the planet is an outstanding characteristic of life.

Another special feature is that while the non-living things in Nature like mountains gradually erode and finally vanish, living things not only maintain themselves but actively grow and evolve as long as they have continuous inputs of energy and molecules from outside themselves.

Each cell is a complex unit whose working parts are literally responsible for keeping the whole cell in the condition we define as alive. They contain a lot of chemical machinery which must be positioned, maintained and regulated to do the various jobs -- many of which are precisely the maintenance of the cell and therefore of the machinery itself. Each is a tiny chemical factory that is essentially dependent on its own output products.

Over the long history of life on earth living things became more complex and reached new levels of capacity by increasing the number of cooperating specialized cells to become the highly coordinated and widely adapted multicellular plants that we take for granted today. How the individual cells communicate in a multicellular plant is a great mystery that we have been learning about bit by bit for years but still have only a partial idea of.

One of the great unexplained wonders of the universe is how any plant or animal can start as a single cell, the fertilized egg (properly called a *zygote*) and, by the processes of cell division and specialization, become a mass of billions of cells of a multicellular organism that somehow still function as a single integrated entity. What is this *force* (we don't even have a really good term for it since *spirit, soul, being* all have overtones that make them inadequate) that inhabits each of the cells and yet goes beyond the individual cells to be the motivating, energizing, and encompassing life principle of the organism as a whole? To date no one knows. Possibly we never will. The natural sciences might never be able to tell us because the answer may lie in some level that cannot be measured, manipulated, and experimented with by our technical tools and so is simply outside the province of science. It is hard to decide which is the more marvelous creature, the microscopic unicellular species that accomplishes all of the functions of life within that single microscopic mass or the multicellular creature accomplishing as a unit all of the tasks being done by the unicellular species and a whole range of other tasks that those cannot even dream of.

The worlds of unicellularity and multicellularity have many things in common but they are also remarkably different in many details. Multicellular living things are faced with the problem of making a variety of specialized structures needed for particular jobs when they are limited in the size of the units of material that they can move outside their living matter and still assemble and precisely control even at a distance.

For several good reasons that we will consider below, the basic functional parts of living things must be microscopically small to work well. Cells are able to assemble most of the required parts from within rather than having them extruded and transported from "master units" somewhere in the vicinity. This is not a simple decision to implement because it means that there must be instructions produced and retained for how each specialized cell type will develop from the starting general form that results from fertilization and, at least as complicated, a regulatory mechanism to determine which cells will develop into which specialized type so there are the proper number in the right places to do the needed jobs without a lot of interference, waste, and clutter. That, we believe, is what was going on in those impossible-to-grasp long periods of evolutionary time as a lot of mistakes were made and died but the remaining creatures gradually accumulated the necessary genetic know-how and changed or improved in the ways we see in the fossils and among the variety of surviving types as they went from simple to complex.

This dedication to a particular job to the extent of forming structures precisely geared to do that job and thereby giving up the chance to develop into any other specialized form makes sense only in an organism with enough cells to have the required number devoted to each essential task. In a division-of-labor-society all will perish if any one essential job is not being done efficiently enough.

You cannot see a plant without seeing its cells, but you never really see them without the magnification of a microscope. It is at the cellular level that the most striking differences between plants and animals are seen. These differences explain most of the ones seen at the level of the whole multicellular organisms, Plant cells perform many chemical reactions that are identical to those in animal cells and some that animals do not perform such as photosynthesis but most plants do not need some of the animals' functions like the digestion of whole foreign tissues to supply fuel or building materials molecules.

In many places in the multicellular plant the cells cannot be replaced as readily as animal cells. In an animal, fibroblast cells will migrate by way of the blood stream into an area that has been damaged and form new connective tissue ending in scar tissue. There is less chance for that kind of internal repair in plants if the damage is not close to the cambium layer although there are scattered undifferentiated parenchyma cells that remain among the mature tissue cells for a long time to do some of this kind of repair.

Only cells can reproduce. Whether the task is accomplished by mitotic cell division or meiosis followed by fertilization it is single cells that do the job. A large structure can only be replaced by duplicating it one cell at a time.

A question that often arises is *Why are there a lot of small cells rather than one or a few big ones?* There is not one answer to that but four, each a factor that contributes to the advantage of the pattern Nature has gone with.

First there is the surface area to volume ratio. It is a physical fact that if you divide a mass into smaller units (like slicing a loaf of bread), you increase the total amount of surface area within it (by adding all those sides of the slices). It is a chemical reality that most of the chemical reactions that occur in cells do so at some surface, either a membrane or the protein skeleton, since it is easier to control three-dimensional molecules there and make the processes efficient. Together these lead to the limitation on cells that the more interior surface there is, the more chemical reactions can occur every second. This is the simplest explanation for the fact that cells are designed to have large amounts of internal membrane surface. With the electron microscope we found that a typical cell is not a cube of solid protoplasm, it is like a piece of Swiss cheese with membrane-lined canals called the endoplasmic reticulum running all through the mass and greatly increasing the amount of internal surface. In addition a group of small cells has many times as much external surface as a single large cell would have.

Second, there is safety in numbers. If a plant has thousands of cells specialized to do a particular job and several dozen of them die, the plant survives without much trouble. But if it has only two such cells and one of them dies the plant is in grave danger as a result of that single event.

Third, the molecules it needs cannot travel far enough fast enough to keep a large call supplied and in touch with itself. We can measure how fast various molecule types can move into, out of, and around inside cells and we find that many raw materials could not get to the parts of the cell where they are needed, the products and waste by-products of the processes could not be distributed or disposed of fast enough, and the mechanisms that must turn various gene systems on and off to maintain the critical internal chemical environment of the cell could not get the feedback information fast enough if the cells were very large.

Fourth, there is the matter of specialization. Biologists make the generalization that function follows form (or the reverse statement) to indicate that the cellular machinery must be shaped in the way that allows it to do the required jobs most efficiently. A device that does sixteen jobs seldom does many of them, let alone all of them, with high efficiency. Having many cells allows as many specialist types as needed to be produced, sometimes including types so devoted to a particular task that they need nursemaids or cannot survive on their own for long. The most primitive types of multicellular algae have only a small number of recognizably different cell types but a highly evolved type like Rose has many more -- and she can do many more kinds of things as a result.

CHAPTER 4

THIS IS ROSE'S CELL WALL

One of the most characteristic features marking Rose as a plant rather than an animal at the microscopic level is that all her cells have secreted cell walls, semi-rigid boxes, around themselves. These give each cell a shape with six or more definite flat sides. The walls of adjacent cells are glued together by a layer of sticky material called pectin to produce the larger shapes of her leaves, stems, flowers and roots.

Cell walls were what Robert Hooke actually observed in the slice of cork that he described in his *Micrographia* which he published in 1665. He referred to the spaces he could see in it under his microscope as *cells* since they were orderly arranged like the rooms of monks in a monastery and the name cell stuck. It may have been 1772 when Bonaventuri Corti observed movement of the material inside living cells before the importance of the protoplasm in plant cells was fully appreciated.

Cell walls, like so many things, have their advantages and disadvantages. Their big advantage is that they allow Rose to resist the pull of gravity and hold her stems and leaves out where they get the best light for photosynthesis and hold her flowers where they have the best chance of being pollinate and all of this without benefit of muscles. We animals maintain an upright posture by continuous partial contraction of groups of muscles -- and muscle contractions require energy from food fuel and they lead to fatigue. A plant maintains its upright posture simply because it is stacks of rigid boxes glued one on top of another. It is the difference between a stack of basketballs in cartons and a stack of just basketballs -- for some jobs having flat sides and rigidity helps.

Cell walls allow trees to stand upright for a thousand years and never get tired. The price for that is that these walls also keep the plant from dancing a polka or sitting down. They give shape, strength, and protection to the cells but they also add weight and limit the movements of the plant's body parts.

A rigid exterior shape in itself is not an absolute sentence to an unmoving prison since the *Arthropods* (the insects, spiders, crabs, and their like) have rigid exterior shapes because of their "shells" or exoskeletons yet they are a most successful group with more species and larger numbers than all the other higher animal forms put together. They resolve their mobility problem by using jointed legs to walk and jump in spite of their fixed shapes. The critical difference is that plants are "boxed" internally as well, arthropods are not.

Plant materials and insects preserve well in museum collections and dried floral arrangements for the same reason--each gets its overall shape from a rigid external layer that resists decay long after the soft internal materials have dried up. In fact because of her cell walls Rose's parts will still look the same after 200 years if you press them to remove the water and carefully store them in a dry place as is done in herbariums where plant specimens are preserved for scientific study. The resistant parts are likewise responsible for the fine detail preserved in many fossils of plants and the ancestors of the bugs and lobsters. The waxy cell walls of pollen make them particularly good candidates for preservation as fossil material.

The limits on movement that cell walls impose means that the migration of cells into new positions that is common and very important in animal embryos is not feasible in developing plants.

Animal cells have species, individual, and even organ recognition marker molecules on the outside because they may move around themselves or have motile white blood cell "police" from the immune system come by and check their credentials regularly. Plant cells do not have such defender cells that can move around or make those identity inspections so they can do without those external markers and can cover themselves with a cell wall and leave little space between them without interfering with those processes.

The wall provides an additional protection against microbial invaders unless they have cellulases, specific enzymes to dissolve the wall materials. There is even some evidence that in seedlings the cell walls transmit some light to body parts still underground, a method suggestive of fiber-optic systems.

The cell wall limits the size of the cell but also strengthens it and prevents it from being ruptured by an excessive intake of water. As water enters the cell by osmosis a pressure builds that opposes and will eventually slow the water movement to an equilibrium condition. The shape is seldom so rigid that there is not a bit of play so that it can give a bit before stresses like the wind.

The cells are flexible when young but become fixed in size and shape at an early stage because of the cell wall. This structure therefore also limits the plant's growth potential to mainly the young tissues of the terminal meristems and requires some special chemical maneuvers even there.

The wall's main construction is not terribly different than that of the sheet of paper on which you are reading this. In fact the paper is one of more than 4500 products we use, ranging from lumber through cotton, rayon, cellophane, and many industrial chemicals, that are made from plant cell walls.

The principal ingredient of plant cell walls is cellulose, a molecule with special properties. It is a polysaccharide or "multiple sugar" molecule which means it is a large structure formed by bonding together into a continuous chain or polymer a group of small *simple sugar* or monosaccharide molecules, the basic structural units of the carbohydrate molecule type family.

Cellulose is actually a loose family of similar molecule types because, depending on the species making it, from 1000 to as many as 10,000 molecules of glucose are joined to form a single molecule of each form of cellulose.

The wall is formed by the cell that it encloses. The process of assembling cellulose occurs right at the outer membrane of the cell with the long molecules being "spun" into the space outside. Many fibers of cellulose are laid down to form a flat layer in the mortar mix referred to as hemicelluloses that then holds all the components together. The straight unbranched chains of cellulose facilitate its close packing into flat structures called microfibrils. These thin groups are then twisted into thicker cables or macrofibrils that have the tensile strength of steel even though they are made of sugar. In the fibrils the chains are strongly hydrogen bonded to one another along their length which makes them hard to disrupt. This property of cellulose gives it strength with enough pliability to bend a bit rather than snap.

Every change in the number, the kind, or the three dimensional arrangement of the atoms within it produces a different kind of molecule. We know this because each has a unique combination of chemical and physical properties that allow us to separate them. The cellulose molecule has properties different from those of the separate glucose sugar molecules that were joined to form it.

Glucose is the six-carbon monosaccharide molecule type that is formed by plants during photosynthesis and the one that plants and animals like us "burn up" in our cells to release energy. Glucose can have its parts rearranged into seven other three dimensional configurations that are the other hexoses or six-carbon sugars found in Nature. When combined in various branched or unbranched chains the different hexoses and some five-carbon monosaccharides or pentoses allow the formation of a wide variety of large polysaccharides or complex carbohydrates, each with a unique set of chemical and physical properties. It is this variety of end products formed from only simple chain polymers of a small number of stock parts that allow cells to produce the carbohydrate with exactly the size and properties to do each particular job.

The small glucose molecule is put into storage inside a cell by combining it with other molecules of glucose or the other hexoses to form polysaccharides like starches or cellulose or by chemically converting its molecules into those of fats. The starch and cellulose molecules may have exactly the same number of identical glucose units, and the glucose molecules produced when starch and cellulose are disassembled are exactly the same and all equally usable by cells as fuel, but the polymers have strikingly different properties.

For one thing virtually any living thing -- plant or animal, single celled or multicellular -- can break apart or digest the starch for food or fuel. The direct use of cellulose, the most abundant naturally occurring polysaccharide in the world and therefore potentially the largest food supply, however, is restricted to a small group of one-celled species that are the only ones other than the plants that synthesize them that have the necessary enzymes to break the connecting bonds and digest the molecule into the glucose units. The cellulose, in fact, is what makes up the "bulk" and the "fiber" in your diet. It is useful to animal digestive systems precisely because it is not broken up as it passes down the food tube and therefore it gives the gut wall something to push against in order to move material down the tube.

The reason it takes special enzymes to digest is a difference in the three-dimensional position of the bonding connections between the glucose molecules in the cellulose polymer, not some change in the sugar molecules themselves. But what a practical difference that makes.

Another important feature resulting from that special bonding angle is that cellulose will not dissolve in water even though most starches will. This is what makes cellulose such an important structural material and why it is formed in the *outer* part of each cell. Without that property the wall would dissolve in the rain and no land plant could be more than a few layers of cells thick. Try to imagine what the earth would look like with only a microscopically thin green layer anywhere on dry land. Or imagine living in a house made of sugar cubes instead of wood (which is mostly cell walls) and you can appreciate what a difference the cell walls make and why cellulose is so important to the plants and to us. Cellulose does not dissolve but the meshwork of fibrils absorbs a lot of water which it essentially holds in storage.

The appearance and chemical composition of the cell walls varies between tissues within the same plant. A variety of other substances are essential parts of the wall, especially of the mortar holding things together. The components of plant cell walls are not as regularly and tightly bonded together as those in a bacterial cell wall but they still form a strong, stable meshwork.

The spaces between the cellulose fibrils are filled with a continuous jelly-like *matrix* formed of polymers of five-carbon monosaccharides or pentoses and called *cellusans* or pentosans plus a family of structurally similar molecule types called the *pectic substances* because they include pectin. This latter family includes polymers formed of pentoses, hexoses, or a combination of the two. The family all have negative charges which makes them combine readily with water. They bind structures in all dimensions around them which makes them good mortar since they readily form a jelly-like matrix filler. Their charge also lets them combine easily with calcium, magnesium, and other metal ions. Even seen under the electron microscope, masses of these substances are *amorphous*, showing no distinct and predictable shape although of course the atoms within any particular molecule are precisely positioned.

Hemicelluloses is a collective term for the cellusans, pectic substances, and some other molecule types related to those groups that are more readily soluble than cellulose which allows them to be separated from the fibrils. These may function as stored food and be reabsorbed into the cell to be used as needed.

Up to ten percent of the dry weight of cell walls may be proteins, most linked to polysaccharides to form structural glycoproteins. One of these proteins somewhat resembles collagen, the most common protein in the matrix holding animal cells together.

Plant cell walls can withstand internal pressures five times greater than the air pressure in a car tire but sometimes they have to be able to loosen up. A special protein produced when the cell needs to expand is therefore named *expansin*. It temporarily loosens the hydrogen bonds holding the cellulose fibers to other components within the matrix. As internal fluid pressure pushes on the weakened walls they stretch but do not rupture while forming new, longer cellulose fibers that will now make the wall permanently longer. Even when applied to dead stems that are being pulled expansin makes the cell walls stretch noticeably.

Cutin is a fatty non-carbohydrate material used as waterproofing in the cuticle that covers the outer surface of the epidermal cell walls of the stems and leaves. Suberin is a similar component of the cork cells that encase nearly all perennial roots and stems. In some species the cell wall may also contain silica, various waxes, tannins, gums, and mucilages.

The lignins, which are beaten out only by cellulose for the title of most abundant polymer molecule type in plants, are branched chains of the molecule phenyl propane. They are not carbohydrates. The formation of these rigid molecules that bind in all dimensions within the matrix increases the hardness, firmness and strength of the cell walls.

Although relatively inflexible and insoluble, cell walls are not impermeable. The wall's job is to give shape and strength to the cell, not to control what chemicals can enter or leave so it is full of holes and freely allows many materials to pass through in either direction. The thick, sticky matrix jelly probably does affect the ability of some molecule types to penetrate to the plasma membrane and somewhat channel the movement of water within the plant, however. Large molecules like many proteins probably have a hard time entering cells and when secreted must do so by way of special channels or openings.

The *middle lamella* is the thin layer of pectin between adjacent cell walls that is not considered to be part of either cell although it is secreted by them. Between young cells this layer is soft and jelly-like pectin; later it is replaced with a harder cement containing stiffer calcium and magnesium pectate.

The primary wall is the first layer of wall formed. It is thin and contains mostly cellulose embedded in a dense and amorphous hydrogel of hemicelluloses and pectic compounds. The proportions of the components vary from species to species. The primary wall is flexible and elastic within limits. It can increase in area and may exhibit reversible changes in thickness.

The cellulose fibrils provide the basic orientation for the layer. As the cell swells with water more cellulose layers are added. Initially the primary wall has fibrils in a loose, more or less random arrangement. With cell elongation many of these are rearranged around the short dimension of the call where they will best resist any tendency of the cell to expand in that dimension, thus promoting the increase in size in one direction. This stretching of the cell by turgor means an increase in volume without the need to make large volumes of new protoplasm.

As the cell matures more fibrils are deposited in layers over the old ones and many of the older ones will be rearranged to lie parallel to the long dimension of the cell so they prevent further elongation. This rearrangement requires the breaking of chemical bonds by enzymes and then formation of new ones but the details of how that happens are not known.

Mature cells that retain their living protoplasts (like fruits, leaves, fleshy stems and roots) have only primary walls since hardening of their cell wall is neither needed nor desirable. This also allows the cells to "undifferentiate". divide, and differentiate into new cell types if necessary for wound healing or regeneration of destroyed parts.

A secondary wall is laid down only after the cell is finished growing. It is inside the primary wall which is inside the middle lamella. It is thicker than the primary wall, and it contains more cellulose but little of the pectic substances so it is often quite rigid and not readily stretched. It has three not easily separable layers with most of the cellulose fibrils parallel in each layer but laid down at different angles in the separate layers to produce a laminated effect for greater strength without additional material. It shows no reversible thickness changes and has little ability to increase in area. Often it is also lignified. When it is produced, lignin infiltrates first the middle lamella, then the primary wall and finally the secondary wall so the cell hardens from the outside in.

Secondary walls are particularly important in strengthening and fluid-conducting cells in which the cell may die and leave only the cell wall "skeleton" to do the job. This is what wood is all about.

Plasmodesmata (from the Greek meaning "molded or formed bands or chains") are very thin strands of cell membrane and protoplasm that pass through holes in the cell walls to interconnect adjacent cells. These are formed during cell division when sections of the endoplasmic reticulum membrane system are "caught" as the new cell plate is being formed across the center of the dividing cell from a mass of protein microtubules and small membrane sacs or *vesicles* from the dictyosomes deep in the cell. The vesicles release pectic substances that become the new middle lamella and their membrane sections join to form the new sections of plasma membrane on the opposite sides of that layer. This is followed quickly by the formation of the new primary walls between the middle lamella and the membrane on each side even while the original cell is elongating as it becomes two separate new cells. The strands may also form between the walls of non-dividing cells when it is necessary to allow transport of molecules between them.

Each plasmodesma (the singular of that rather strange looking name) is a tube within a tube. Each opening in the cell wall for one is lined with cell plasma membrane and this has a separate tube of endoplasmic reticulum membrane referred to as a *desmotubule* extending from cell to cell through it. This means that in a real and literal sense all the protoplasm in the cells that are so connected (the group referred to as a *symplast*) is a single greatly extended cell.

These strands pass through thin areas in the primary wall called primary pits where no secondary wall forms. The pits of adjacent cells are usually lined up to allow the plasmodesmata to make easy connections without being stressed by twists.

The numbers of these strands vary from a few to many depending on the species and the tissue but some cells have one half or more of their total cell surface devoted to them, which can mean 20,000 strands per cell. As we would expect for cells that are not intended to stay connected to one another, there are no plasmodesmata between the cells that will form pollen and eggs These passages let water, ions, hormones, nutrients and even some viruses pass from cell to cell but not large organelles like mitochondria or chloroplasts. So there is an extensive circulation of materials within the network of interconnected cells without the problems of crossing membrane barriers. This interconnectedness may play a role in regulating the vascular system or parts of the overall plant's metabolism.

Although the cellulose has considerable resistance to being stretched it has limited strength to prevent it from being bent along its length. Consequently, when the only thing maintaining the shape of a plant part is the cell walls it may become deformed because of its own weight. This is what happens when a plant wilts. But we all know that a plant wilts because it has become too dry, so what does that have to do with cell walls? A lot. Because the unreinforced cell wall depends on the internal water pressure of the cell (called turgor pressure) to keep it rigid and firm. The center of most mature plant cells is a large, membrane-enclosed water bubble called the *central vacuole*. When this is full of water it fills out the cell, pushing the cytoplasm firmly up against the inside of the cell wall.

The analogy most useful in understanding what happens in the cell is that of a tire with an inner tube. When the inner tube is fully inflated it holds the tire in shape. When the internal air pressure of the inner tube drops, however, there is only the strength of the tire itself to hold up not only the tire but the weight of the whole car. And the tire is simply not designed to bear that much weight so it is deformed and the car is immobilized. In a comparable way, the water-filled cell helps maintain the shape of its own cell wall. The water supports much of the weight because it distributes the force to all parts of the cell wall and down through the columns of cells to the ground. Since a liquid cannot be compressed (the physical fact that lets us raise a car on a hydraulic hoist in a garage by applying pressure to a liquid) the cells maintain their shape and consequently so do the plant parts containing those cells. But if the water pressure drops there are only the cell walls to support the weight of the whole plant part and they are not that strong so they are deformed and the plant wilts until the internal water pressure builds up again.

To avoid this wilting problem some plants invest energy in synthesizing lignins to reinforce the cell walls and form wood which is strong enough to hold up the plant part even when the living material of the cell has died and degenerated so there is no longer any turgor pressure to assist.

CHAPTER 5

THESE ARE ROSE'S CELL MEMBRANES

Biological systems work within and therefore reflect the physical facts of the world. Membranes for instance are reminders that oil and water do not mix. That fact is fundamental to their usefulness and almost certainly reflects how cells began to form at the very beginning. It can be argued that membranes permit life and are absolutely essential to it by establishing an inside distinct from the outside. *Membrane* itself comes from a Latin word meaning skin.

Take a basic divider layer, add some passages to permit controlled access of non-lipid soluble molecule types, and you have a self-contained new chemical world on a microscopic level. An outer surface which can anchor proteins without seriously disrupting the lipid components inevitably becomes a display surface for identification badges and specific message receptors precisely because that is the only part of the unit the outside world can contact. Some proteins penetrate the entire membrane and act as channels that allow passage of specific molecule types through the layers in both directions. Internally the membranes are the logical places to gather the various parts of the necessary synthetic assembly lines so that the operations can go on efficiently instead of sporadically as would be the case if all the enzymatic machinery were free floating in a watery soup.

The complexity of biological membranes comes from the variety of protein, carbohydrate, and lipid molecule types that create its third dimension rather than from the architecture of the relatively flat sheets of material in the other dimensions. The differences in their structural components allow a range of flexibilities of the flat surfaces to be coupled with an enormous variety of channels, receptors, ID markers, and attachment units without interfering with the conspicuous dividing and packaging functions that seem so natural a use for wide sheets of material. In fact many of those functions would be difficult to carry out except on a flat surface.

In rough analogy the diversity of component parts in biological membranes is like the variety we see in a species like ourselves. We are all easily identified as members of the human species and no other surviving one but we represent a great many individual variations on the basic human body pattern in size, shape, color, and other features large and small. And just as the many proteins and other membrane components do a long list of different tasks, the various people around us do many different and often highly specialized jobs in society. This is complexity within a framework of simplicity or at least relative uniformity.

In a real and literal sense the outer or plasma membrane is the major door person that regulates much of what enters and leaves any cell. It forms a barrier that confines the cytoplasm to maintain its integrity, regulates the passage of molecules in and out, and provides attachment sites for a large number of kinds of identification, channel-forming, and catalytic proteins and protein-complexes.

The plasma membrane influences the formation of aggregates or groupings of cell into tissues because similar cells must be able to recognize one another even through cell walls and often must literally stick together by means of specialized areas. They may also form microvilli, tiny finger-like folds of the membrane that increase the surface area without increasing the overall volume. This lets them increase the rate of absorption into the cell or of chemical activity at the internal membrane surface.

Membranes surround the eucaryotic cell as a whole and also divide it internally into compartments that are morphologically and metabolically distinct -- i.e. they form the various membrane-enclosed organelles that we recognize by their size and shape with the electron microscope and we now know that distinctly different chemical processes are going on within each type. A eucaryotic cell is a house with several rooms and the movement of molecules into and out of each is regulated so that certain materials may be released within the cell but not be allowed to leak out of it and others can be taken in from outside but kept from entering certain of the compartments where they might disrupt the specialized activities there. Not all cell structures are enclosed by specific membranes though. Ribosomes, for instance, are not.

Membranes are the boundaries but also parts of the working organelles within the cytoplasm. These living wrappers package and regulate the movement of materials across them -- which means letting things in or out as well as keeping things in or out and being able to change the specifications of what can pass in either direction as needed. This compartmentalization improves the efficiency of the cell by allowing sections to be specialized for particular jobs and marks the major step upward from procaryotic to eucaryotic cells. It is not surprising then to find that the internal membranes have different permeabilities, each allowing only certain molecule types in or out according to the needs of that organelle no matter what any other membrane will permit.

The typical biological membrane is now believed to be a double layer of phospholipid molecules with a variety of protein and carbohydrate molecule types sticking to it or penetrating one or both layers. Specifically the basic form or *unit membrane* consists of two layers of lipid with their hydrophobic tails facing one another. Think of a large number of clothespin-shaped units with magnets in their "leg" ends that are free to move in three dimensions. The magnets attract one another but there are too many units to form a tight circle so they will end up jostling one another into a double layer with the magnetized legs inside and the neutral head ends outside. This is similar to what happens to form biological membranes except that it is water-loving *(hydrophilic)* and water-hating *(hydrophobic)* ends rather than magnets that drive the movements. Even in a test tube these molecules will spontaneously arrange themselves to enclose a mass of water and water-soluble molecules to form a preliminary cell type unit because when the tails are intertwined the molecules are in their stable, lowest energy configuration so they tend to stay that way.

Long before we had any visual confirmation of the double lipid layer there were indirect hints of it. In 1925 Dutch scientists E. Gorter and F. Grendel measured the amount of lipid in the membranes of human red blood cells and found that there was twice as much lipid present as the total membrane surface of the cells would hold so it had to be present as a bilayer. An interesting quirk of their work is that they made two errors that would have seriously skewed their measurements but by happy coincidence the two mistakes effectively corrected one another and left their conclusion intact and correct.

The most abundant molecule types in biological membranes by numbers, typically more than fifty percent of the total, are the several kinds of lipids that form the matrix or continuous thin layers. Many membranes contain as much as four times the amount of protein as lipid by weight although there are some that have a greater proportion of lipid. The important distinction here is that the protein molecules typically are ten to a hundred times as large and heavy as the membrane lipid molecule types so even when there is much more protein by weight those are almost always going to be a smaller number of molecules.

A large percentage of the membrane lipids are phospholipids, large molecules that have fatty acid molecules, long chains of carbon and hydrogen atoms, attached to two of the carbon atoms of a three-carbon backbone molecule while a phosphate group (and in some forms additional groups) is attached to the third. This is the same basic construction used in the triglycerides, the types of fats we use for energy storage and insulation, except that in those there are three fatty acids attached and no phosphate unit.

The structure is critical because it gives the molecule its polarity -- the backbone end of the molecule is hydrophilic while the hydrocarbon tails or fatty acids are hydrophobic. The hydrocarbon interior of the bilayer makes it an effective barrier because it is impermeable to most biological molecule types which are soluble in water but not in lipids.

Different nitrogen-containing groups bonded to the phosphate unit will produce different phospholipid types. So will having a different three-carbon backbone chain. Glycerol is the backbone of most of the dietary fats as well as some common phospholipid types. Adding a specific group to convert the phosphate grouping into choline produces the phospholipid lecithin (now famous as the component of no-stick cooking spray). Sphingolipids on the other hand have a three-carbon chain called sphingosine as their backbone.

It must be kept in mind that molecule types are classified as lipids because of their insolubility in water, not because they are all similar in structure. Varying amounts of steroid and cholesterol molecules, large lipid types very different in shape from the phospholipids but still with hydrophobic and hydrophilic ends, are often packed in between the tail chains of the phospholipids in a membrane.

A typical unit membrane bilayer is mostly glycerol-based phospholipids plus varying amounts of sphingoliopids and cholesterol. Plasma membranes seem to contain more cholesterol and sphingolipids than many internal ones.

The Fluid Mosaic Model of membrane structure derives its name from the observations that sometimes in the laboratory two different kinds of cells can be induced to merge and when that happens the surface features of the two fused cells quickly mingle and spread themselves around the combined cytoplasm in a way that suggests the outer layer is a fluid rather than a solid material. Also, except during the organized chaos of cell division, new material seems to be added to membranes uniformly as if it can be fitted in anywhere rather than only at special spots. The fact that the layer is self-sealing adds to the image of a loose or fluid composition.

Imagine a bathtub with the water surface loosely covered with a layer of ping-pong balls. This is a working analogy of the fluid phospholipid layer of a membrane. If we place a wind-up toy ducky in there it can swim all around because the ping pong balls, which are not attached to one another, move out of its way and close in behind it again so they self seal the opening it makes. Voila! A protein moves laterally across a cell membrane.

We know that indeed many, if not most, of the protein and lipid molecules can move laterally within the membrane structure although recent studied suggest there may be many domains that last for various periods of time that limit the movement of some of the proteins to localized regions. We are becoming more aware of a protein cytoskeleton that exists inside (not within) many and possibly all plasma membranes. It seems that at least some of the membrane proteins form attachments to this geodesic-dome type structure of thin protein rods or tubes and that this is what keeps them from drifting randomly among the lipid units but it also seems to provide a guide-rail path along which the protein can be moved rapidly to new locations when that is needed.

Water passes through lab-made phospholipid bilayers at about the same rate as it does through natural membranes. The passage is rapid which means that the lipid layer is not nearly as waterproof as we expect. The water may enter between the lipid molecules as they move about or there may be unrecognized permanent pores that it can enter through. The amount of cholesterol in the membrane affects the passage of water probably by reducing the frequency of small momentary openings in the lipid barrier since it fits into spaces between the tails of the phospholipids. In general the more fluid or flexible the membrane, the more readily water passes through it. Not surprisingly warmer water enters faster since its molecules are more energetic. This also demonstrates that the movement is by osmosis rather than any active process. Not as obvious is the fact that more unsaturated fatty acids in the membrane also increases the ease of water passage. Possibly this is because unsaturated fatty acid chains form kinks or bends where their carbon-to-carbon double bonds occur and therefore they are not able to be packed as tightly together.

The flexibility of the plasma membrane is shown in plasmolysis when the protoplast shrinks as water leaves if the tissue is placed in salt water and can stretch again as fast as the water is restored. But how is this possible since there must be a continuous layer of phospholipid to keep water from entering freely? It must somehow fold in on itself as the cytoplasm rapidly shrinks and unfold as it re-expands.

Membrane associated molecules are involved in much of the chemistry going on in any living thing because it is easier to control molecules in 3-D at a surface and control is all important to a cell and life. The chemical reactions affecting passage through or using enzymes and other molecules embedded in a membrane are common but few reactions seem to involve the phospholipid molecules themselves. The lipids form the matrix but the proteins carry out the specific functions of the membranes.

The kinds of proteins and complexes differ at the two membrane surfaces. Like the lipids, some proteins that stick through the membrane have hydrophilic and hydrophobic ends that assure they will be pushed through the bilayer right end out (although it takes a few molecular tricks to get the water-loving end through the lipid core). Carbohydrates may attach to either proteins to form glycoproteins or lipids to form glycolipids but these types are almost always only on the outer surface. There are also differences in the lipid composition of the cytoplasmic and extracellular faces of plasma membranes. Just why there need to be several types of phospholipids and why the amounts of the various types are consistently different in the inner and outer layers of the bilayer are matters still to be answered. We do know that cells increase the proportion of unsaturated or kinked fatty acids when the temperature drops because otherwise the membranes become too rigid. We can assume all the differences in their chemical and physical properties are for this type of reason but we do not yet understand many of the details.

Receptors are found for molecules like hormones which targets them only to specific tissues. Most known receptors are proteins but some involve lipids. A change in permeability produced by some receptors results from the reversible opening of gated channels in the plasma membrane. The various channels or pores can be shown to admit only specific molecule types. They regulate what passes through them on the basis of the size and often the charge of the molecule.

Although not every known carrier type is a protein, for several reasons those are a logical choice for making most of the carriers or channels to transport molecules across membranes. Proteins can be very precise and specific about what molecule types they bind to (the necessary way for molecule types to identify one another) because they have three dimensional shape that can have precisely positioned positive and negative electric charges, hydrophobic and hydrophilic regions, and various reactions groups so they can distinguish between quite similar molecule types and also find the ones that fit among large numbers of ones that do not. They can also rapidly and reversibly change their affinity for a molecule type as a result of interactions with other molecules or environmental factors, an important trait for structures that must grab onto other molecules to confirm their fit but must release them again at the appropriate point in the process.

Also by acting as catalysts, proteins can make some active transport processes possible by coupling together two operations, one of which will occur without much persuasion and will release some energy but the other of which requires that energy to make it happen under normal conditions.

And since proteins are the direct products of genes they are very straightforwardly formed. Most non-protein molecule types that might function as transport carriers would require several steps, each regulated by a different enzyme, to synthesize so using proteins conserves energy and genome space. And finally, since proteins are readily made the cell can regulate the rate of transport of particular materials efficiently by altering the number of membrane channels, making or destroying some as needed.

Oxygen, carbon dioxide, and nonpolar organic molecules dissolve easily in lipid and pass relatively unhindered through biological membranes but the plasma membrane controls the distribution of inorganic ions like potassium (K^+), hydrogen (H^+), sodium (Na^+) and chloride (Cl^-) that are important in regulating water balance and have a direct effect on enzyme activities and other processes inside the cell and in the spaces around them. In the process they affect the composition of the fluid being transported through the plant body as they add or remove molecules in a controlled way.

Although the receptors that are actually detectors of specific molecule types by shape are almost universally proteins the molecules they are designed to recognize and bind to are often carbohydrates. Because simple sugar (or monosaccharide) and other carbohydrate molecules can be linked together to form polymers or chains at either of several places around their 3-D shape the number of overall 3-D macromolecule types they can form as groups is much greater than the already staggeringly large number of different proteins that can be formed by linking together amino acid molecules that have only one spot each where they will fit into a polymer. Carbohydrates can form branched as well as straight chain polymers and even short sequences of them therefore have a unique 3-D shape, the trait needed for a precision identification system. The diverse group of proteins known collectively as lectins can each recognize and bind to a specific type of carbohydrate molecule or a configuration of two or more linked ones including glycoproteins or glycolipids. A variety of lectins are present on plant cell membrane surfaces so they are presumably important in establishing who is who and who will connect with whom in the plant body.

Selective permeability tends to produce an imbalance of electric charges across biological membranes. Because most of the large biological molecule types like proteins and nucleic acids and many of the small ones like nucleotides and phosphorylated carbohydrates have overall negative charges these simply outnumber the positively charged ions resulting in a -20 to -100 millivolt potential difference across the plasma membrane of many cells. This charge has a role in active transport of some types. Since the membrane is relatively impermeable to cations like Na^+ and Ca^{+2} neutralization of the charges does not occur easily.

Gradients of ions like sodium (Na^+) and potassium (K^+)--and hydrogen (H^+) in bacteria -- are a way a cell stores energy to use in other functions. The co-transport systems contain a protein channel that moves two specific molecule types across the membrane simultaneously. In a typical case sodium ions (Na^+) move by diffusion from an area of higher concentration on one side of the membrane to an area of lower concentration on the other side and that pulls a sugar, amino acid, or other molecule along with it. If the gradient is not maintained so that Na^+ diffusion can continue, transport of the other molecule types stops. The system therefore must use ATP energy to run sodium ion pumps that move enough Na^+ back out of the cell to keep the concentrations different.

Ion gradients are automatically also electrochemical ones, both resulting from the different concentrations of ions on the two sides of a membrane so that the charges create an electrical potential. Both the difference in ion concentration and the electrical potential can be harnessed by the cell to do work. An electrical potential is an electric field that can influence the direction of movement of charged particles. For instance a negatively charged molecule entering a channel is drawn toward the positively charged side of the membrane without the need for any other energy expenditure.

Also the interaction of ions and electrical potentials can alter the shape or proteins and other membrane molecules so an ion gradient may control the opening and closing of channels or change the shape of a protein to favor the association of the transported molecule with the transport system on one side of the membrane but favor its dissociation on the other side.

Electric fields applied from outside have been shown to cause oriented movement of charged proteins in plasma membranes so it is postulated that biologically generated potentials could have a similar effect.

Membranes as outer coverings and inner dividers allow the existence of cells that hold together and that hold everything more or less in place but still are highly flexible. The design is so simple yet complex one might wonder why the direct descendants of what we believe are the oldest cell types, the bacteria, fungi and early algae, all have cell walls enclosing them. The most likely answer is that the additional layer makes for better water regulation in a highly saturated environment since the strong wall gives the membrane something to brace itself against as it resists the tendency of the water pressure inside the cell to rupture the membrane. Animal type cells living in freshwater must more or less continuously pump out excess water, while those living in sea water must take in water regularly to balance the uncontrollable loss of water due to osmosis. Both operations require the use of metabolic energy so they are a cost of doing the business called staying alive. The synthesis of a cell wall also requires an expenditure of food energy and chemical raw materials but once paid for metabolically it can continue to provide essential protection for the cell for an extended period of time with only minimum maintenance costs in the form of some continuing expenditures for repair. This probably makes a cell wall a good investment for a small organism that does not need to move around much to survive. The synthesis of a cell wall may also have been a safer way for early cells to go until they had a chance to develop enough internal complexity to form the various bilge pumps that we find among the protozoans.

CHAPTER 6

THESE ARE ROSE'S ER AND CYTOSKELETON

The necessary qualifications continuously added to statements about cell structures and functions get to be a drag and there is a temptation to shout out, "Why don't you *know* instead of just suspect?" After all, the cells are right there and the researchers have all the tools of modern technology at their disposal so why all the uncertainties? The answer in a word is size. Molecules and individual cells are too small for us to achieve the direct examinations we would like so we have to make do with indirect approaches and there is always then a real and sometimes substantial risk that we will significantly alter the cell parts in preparing them for close examination and will draw the wrong conclusions on the basis of these altered fragments.

To understand the nature of our scientific knowledge you must keep in mind the limitations of the research tools and get a feel for the fact that it takes a prepared mind with considerable imagination to put together in the "mind's eye" an image of the three dimensional apparatus as it functions in the cell from the pieces of information gathered by different techniques and revealing different chemical and structural features. The researchers are as frustrated as the rest of us at not being able to make more definite and universal statements but they accept as we must that scientific certitude extends only as far as the data goes. Beyond that is speculation and although that is a necessary part of the process to determine what to study and how to do so it does not have the same foundation in observation and measurement. But within the limits of the technology we have put together a detailed picture of the operations within a cell.

As we have developed better ways of examining the cell's contents we have found surprise after surprise because so many of the structures that allow it to operate do not show up under the light microscope. In most cases this is because the membranes that limit and therefore define the organelles are too thin to be seen in cross section. The electron microscope let us see such cut membranes and brought into view a variety of parts which were then investigated by chemical analysis after they were separated from intact cells in challenging and often tedious ways.

The task took time and there are still some points about which we hesitate because of the way the analysis has to be done. Even after we have identified a particular kind of bubble in the cell's cytoplasm we have to go through various slash-and-burn type steps to obtain what we think might be a sample of the uncontaminated contents of those bubbles because while we do today have glass needles fine enough to penetrate a single cell and inject some foreign DNA into it we do not have a finely controlled system with which we can suck out the contents of just a few bubbles for chemical analysis -- especially since we can only recognize many of those bubbles in cells killed and stained for viewing under the electron microscope.

Most of our information about cell parts is based on taking some cells and running them through a blender to chop them up (which they undoubtedly hate), then separating the resulting soup into pieces of similar size, a combination of weight and shape, in a centrifuge. Finally just the layer containing the parts or the fragments of parts of interest is removed for chemical analysis. At the largest practical level this means that until we have done a lot of studies just to establish what is present in what form in the soup we have limited confidence that the parts are constructed in the way that we think they are because we have only this debris goulash to put in our testtubes and we may have changed things considerably as we prepared the goop. If you have a strong enough stomach to consider what some gigantic species would think we look like inside and out from running us through a blender and trying to compare the resulting pieces with the views they got when they put thin slices of us under their microscope you get an idea of the conceptual problem.

When a research team has some idea of the exact chemicals that are in the cell part they can use their knowledge of chemistry and the accumulated body of information about molecule types identified in other species and other biological processes to make an educated guess or hypothesis about what these may be doing in this cell and organelle. That suggestion can then be tested by chemically altering intact living cells in ways that we have discovered will affect the process believed to be involved here to see if the cells show signs of an increased or decreased activity of that sort. A change in the cells suggests the hypothesis has some foundation and we proceed. No detectable change in the cells suggests that the hypothesis is wrong and a new one needs to be made to explain what we know about the cells and their internal structures.

Imagine remotely operating a spaceship crewed by robots that has a satellite camera that lets you photograph the structures on a distant planet from high in its sky but each photo will show only a one inch thick horizontal slice through everything in view. This is a rough analogy to what the transmission electron microscope lets us do (except that we have to cut the cells open and chemically treat them rather than just focus into them).

You spot some large, regularly shaped units of interest in some of the views. You decide to call these "buildings" and you want to find out all about them. To do that though you must send in huge machines which will scoop up some of the buildings, smash them to rubble, sift all the material through a series of progressively smaller mesh opening sieves and, using that satellite camera again examine the different piles of debris to see which holds the particular items that have attracted your attention. Your various pictures of the slices and the rubble seem to find two kinds of these long, thin items because on some one end is pointy but on others it is blunt. Chemical analysis of the smallest pile of debris you can produce that includes some of the items suggests they are made of wood but have a pure carbon center, and that the end that is the same in all of them and has a characteristic shape contains rubber. What function can they serve in the factory? Perhaps they are involved in mixing or stirring operations since they are often seen in the camera views of intact buildings inside shallow rectangular depressions, sometimes lying parallel but sometimes in seemingly random arrangements. This is what the cell biologists are up against in trying to understand their chosen level of biology. And to their credit they do make sense of most of it.

The Endoplasmic Reticulum is an extensive system of interconnected membrane-enclosed flattened channels running all through the cytoplasm of eucaryotic cells that are clearly seen only with the electron microscope. It got its name which means "netting in the cytoplasm" because in the Eighteenth century a few researchers reported seeing an indistinct net-like appearance in some cells and compared it to the netting handbags called reticules that the fashionable ladies of the day were carrying. Today we are content to refer to it as the ER (not to be confused with a hospital area or a television show).

A primary function of this organelle is the synthesis of new membrane components for the whole cell, including the conversion of saturated fatty acid molecules to unsaturated ones as needed to match the appropriate lipid composition of the particular membranes. In addition the fluid-filled canal system allows rapid transport of materials from one site to another without disrupting the more rigidly positioned cell structures. The interior space is sometimes used to store synthesized materials where they can be ready to go but cannot interfere with other chemical reactions until they are needed in a hurry. Its cytoplasmic side also provides surface for attachment sites for ribosomes and various enzymes needed for chemical reactions.

Today there seems to be agreement that the ER is continuous with the outer layer of the nuclear membrane but not with the plasma membrane although for many years there was confusion about this. Without direct openings to the outside everything must still pass through the plasma membrane to get in or out of the cell even if it can be transported close to that layer within the ER canals. This extensive system may contain as much as fifty percent of all the membrane in the whole cell including the outer plasma membrane. This means that the interior of a cell is much less solid than we used to think, more like a piece of Swiss cheese than a solid block of protoplasm.

The amount of ER in a cell type reflects the amount of chemical work done by those cells with types that export lipids or proteins showing the largest amounts. In the same way the number of mitochondria in a cell type reflects the amount of mechanical work those cells do.

From the start the electron microscope views showed two fairly distinct types of membranes in the system, rough ER that was lined with many small granules that turned out to be ribosomes, and smooth ER that had no granules. The question to be resolved was whether they were significantly different. To find out they had to chemically analyzed separately. Conveniently, when plant tissues are homogenized for study the ER fragments into *microsomes* or "very small bodies" and the rough and smooth types are readily separated with the centrifuge for analysis. This process also finds that, as would be expected, there is a transitional form connecting the others into a continuous system.

The answer to the question is that they *are* different. Rough ER is characterized by the attachment of ribosomes to the cytoplasmic side of the membrane by their large subunits. Rough ER is the site of the synthesis of virtually all proteins that will leave the cell to do their job or that will be stored within it. In fact these proteins penetrate through the ER membrane as they are being assembled and fold into their functional 3-D shape within the fluid-filled space of the ER canal. Often several such rough ER sacs will lie parallel to one another.

The complete eucaryotic ribosome contains four smaller rRNA subunits and some 80 different proteins. The description of ribosome subunits is the place where many people begin to have their doubts about the ability of cell biologists to add since they tell us that the bacterial 70S ribosome is formed from the combination of a 30S subunit and a 50S subunit and the 80S eucaryotic ribosome combines 60S and 40S subunits. What is seldom explained is that the S represents Svedborg units that are a measure of the relative speed at which particles settle in a tube when centrifuged. Since that measure depends on the shape as well as the mass of the particle there is not a straight numerical correlation between the S value and the weight which we may tend to assume is being compared. Feathers sink slower than sand grains in air or- in the liquid in a centrifuge tube (although not in a vacuum) because of frictional forces on the larger surface.

When not involved in the translation of a messenger RNA (mRNA) into a peptide chain the subunits of the ribosome are separated. The assembly of the full ribosome so it is attached to the lead end of the mRNA is the start of translation process. A special molecule of the amino acid methionine with an extra piece attached was identified in 1964 by K. Marker and F. Sanger as the first unit of every peptide chain during assembly although this initiator is either subsequently cut off or converted to the normal form of that amino acid as part of the process of maturing the finished peptide chain undergoes. As many as ten to twenty ribosomes have been observed attached in sequence along a single mRNA forming a polysome, each ribosome at a different spot in the process of spinning out an identical copy of the same peptide chain since they must always start at the same end of the mRNA.

Ribosomes have the essential enzyme peptidyl transferase that hooks the amino acids together incorporated right into their structure. They hold the other participant molecules in position so that the peptide chain can be assembled rapidly. Depending on the cell type it takes from about ten seconds to two minutes to assemble an average-sized peptide chain, with bacteria generally doing so faster than eucaryotic cells.

Small bacteria can have 5000 to 10,000 ribosomes; large eucaryotic cells can have several million of them with those carrying on a lot of protein synthesis having more than the average. Without ribosomes there is no protein synthesis. The many duplicate copies of the genes specifying the various rRNA types are probably a reflection of the cell's need for many of these functional units.

Typically proteins formed on rough ER enter the lumen and are stored, processed, and/or exported but those formed on free ribosomes stay within the cytoplasm. When stored in the ER space, as happens for instance in many kinds of seeds, proteins may noticeably swell local regions of the ER.

Smooth ER has no ribosomes attached and is particularly involved in lipid metabolism and, in some animal cells at least, detoxification processes. The ER's primary function of making new membrane components for the plasma membrane and for all the organelles occurs here where fatty acid molecules that were synthesized in the cytoplasm are assembled into phospholipids.

The detoxification processes include a variety of enzyme controlled reactions that convert potentially dangerous molecule types into harmless forms. The interesting thing is that some of these reactions are inducible -- the enzyme molecules are quickly formed (or their numbers increased) when the hazardous material enters the cells but are disassembled when they are no longer needed because the hazard has been destroyed. These processes are well studied in animal liver cells and it is not illogical to expect comparable activity in plants but there seems to have been little specific research on it so far.

The smooth ER is also important to the calcium ion (Ca^{+2}) regulation in the cell. This ion has an important role in a number of processes so cells need to be able to store some in a way that will let them release it when they need it but keep it inactive the rest of the time. That is done by combining the ion with either of several protein types designed for that purpose that are bound to the membrane here. When the calcium ion is needed it is released by an enzyme while the sequestering protein remains in place to be used again when extra ions are available.

The other very extensive structural component of the cell interior is not membrane-enclosed and not discrete enough to be nailed down to one spot within the cell. This major part that even the transmission electron microscope did not reveal is the cytoskeleton, a combination of several categories of thin rods and tubules of several different proteins that form a loosely interconnected geodesic dome-type meshwork through most of the cell areas that look under the microscope as if they are general "soup" areas.

The cytoskeleton helps maintain cell shape, contributes to the movement of materials within the cell and probably on the outer membrane surface, allows movement of whole cells of some kinds, and provides attachment sites for a range of enzymes and other molecules. It took special staining using antibodies that bind to only these protein types but could have a fluorescent molecule attached at another spot to reveal these structures that are thinner than membranes. Its presence makes the cell less of a mysterious bag of fluid and more a changeable but architecturally sensible structure so its discovery was almost a relief to many biologists.

The Surface Area to Volume Ratio explains a great many of our questions about why the cell parts, tissues, and whole organs of plants and animals are shaped and arranged as they are. That design maximizes or minimizes the amount of surface area -- and that means mostly membrane surface -- depending on the needs of the organism. We now recognize that most of the thousands and thousands of chemical reactions that must occur every second in each cell to maintain the conditions we call being alive take place at some surface, either a membrane or the cytoskeleton. The chemical reactions occur at surfaces because it is easier that way. The molecules that are going to interact are three dimensional units with a definite shape that is critical to their functioning. Just as our hands but not our shoulders or our knees can grasp another's foot, only specific sections or reactive *sites* of the molecules can interact to form the chemical bond that will hook them together (or separate cleanly from one another when the bond is broken in the reverse reaction).

For molecule A and molecule B to bond together they must bump into one another with enough energy to start the reaction and with the appropriate reactive site of each positioned so they will come in contact. If they are not lined up right they will simply bounce off and no reaction will occur. If they are lined up right but do not have enough energy in their collision they will bounce off and no reaction will occur, like railroad cars that fail to couple when they are bumped together too gently. And for the large three-dimensional shapes of proteins and many of the other macromolecule types that are the characteristic machinery of living things a molecule might by chance only be positioned right a small percent of the times. So if the cell needs this particular reaction to occur at a fast rate to supply the end product molecule or, in break-apart reactions to prevent the buildup of a dangerous molecule type, it needs a mediator to make sure the reagent molecules are positioned right and to make the reaction go. The mediators are catalysts called enzymes. And they are usually attached to some cellular surface, often in assembly line sequence groups, to do their job. They attract the specific molecules and more easily persuade them to combine or split because everything is literally lined up right rather than free floating all around in the watery medium in the cell.

CHAPTER 7

THESE ARE ROSE'S NUCLEUS, CHROMOSOMES AND GENES

The nucleus is a double membrane enclosed region containing the bulk of the cell's DNA. Its presence is used as the defining trait of a eucaryotic cell since only cells that also have the other traits associated with that classification, especially the other organelles, have a nucleus. It is a common belief that every complex system like a living thing needs a control center to coordinate activities by giving appropriate orders based on stored ancestral programs proven by the test of evolutionary survival and on short term feedback information. The higher animals have a brain for this purpose and plant and animal cells have a nucleus.

The nucleus gets its name from the Latin for *kernel* and was surely the first internal structure seen with the light microscope since it is denser that the other parts so it appears as a large dark spot within the cell. It took some time to appreciate its true importance but not because it was being ignored. The organelle occupies from about five to as much as fifty percent of the cell volume depending on species and tissue type. It is a larger part of rapidly dividing meristem cells than of mature cells but a significant part of this is due to the generally smaller size of meristem cells. The nuclear DNA content is almost always twice that of the egg cell of the species no matter what the cell type or visible size of the organelle.

The nucleus is a master archive that stores and protects the condensed and chemically coded record of the evolutionary history leading to this individual. It is continually sending out reports in the form of messenger RNA (mRNA) molecules in response to signals for specific information based on that record that lists the responses that worked in the past and thus are the safest way to go in the present-

There are a very few kinds of eucaryotic cells known that at maturity no longer have a nucleus, our own red blood cells being the most often mentioned example, but all these cells did have a functional nucleus earlier in their development. A functional nucleus is necessary to the long term survival of the cell both to continue its metabolism and to control its various structures and functions. Cells that lose their nucleus as they mature have limited live expectancies and carry on little metabolic activity.

The nucleus can be surgically removed and even transplanted as was done in some early cloning work. Organisms like some fungi and plant gametophytes may have several nuclei within a continuous mass of cytoplasm rather than one nucleus per cell.

Some of the great mysteries of living things are tightly locked in the nucleus -- like how does the cell know which genes to use when? We are working out some of the details today.

The nuclear envelope is a major landmark of evolution since it allows greater efficiency and possibly better regulation than in procaryotic cells. It is a flattened sac consisting of two concentric lipid bilayers, the outer bilayer continuous with the endoplasmic reticcultum and studded with many ribosomes. There is a perinuclear space between the inner and outer membranes that is continuous with ER canal system that extends all through the cytoplasm. The inner bilayer is lined with *nuclear* lamina, a layer of specialized filament proteins and has no ribosomes. Often in electron micrographs the chromatin or DNA seems to be closely associated with the inner surface of the inner membrane.

The nuclear membranes apparently play multiple roles in the regulation of DNA replication and seem critical to limiting DNA replication to one round per cell cycle. The whole envelope disintegrates during cell division and reappears afterwards.

The envelope is penetrated by pore complexes that hold the two bilayers together while they allow the exchange of even large molecules between the nucleus and the cytoplasm. There may be thousands of them occupying from ten to thirty percent of the nuclear envelope surface area. A few cell types like mature sperm cells in which the nucleus is inactive have few pores. Each pore is organized from eight identical pieces fitted together leaving a central channel that is thirty time the size of a ribosome and those structures can in fact pass through the opening.

The complex may serve as a regulated gate since it is shaped like a double iris mechanism on the order of a spaceship airlock. A molecule that includes an essential signal part causes the cytoplasmic side iris to open so that the molecule can enter and then close with the molecule inside. Next the nucleus side iris opens and the molecule moves into the nucleus. Only molecules with a different signal part can make the nucleus side iris open to pass through to the cytoplasm in a similar multistep way.

It is possible that the complex somehow propels the molecule into the nucleus. There are fibrils associated with the complex that may act as tracks for the molecule to move along or they may even move themselves and take attached units with them rather like moving cables taking cable cars along with them. However it works, transport through the complex requires energy delivered by ATPs but the details are still being worked out.

The nucleolus is a distinct, even denser, region of the nuclear contents but it has no membrane separating it from the rest of the nucleus. Some species have more than one nucleolus. These are the sites of the formation of ribosomes, where the ribosomal RNAs and proteins are assembled into the working subunits of those organelles. Nucleoli have long been known to be more prominent in cell types that do much protein synthesis.

There must be a good reason why proteins are not made in the nucleus even though it is all about the information for making proteins. The advantages of having a nucleus set off as a restricted area by a nuclear envelope include the fact that presynthesized transcription factors and cell cycle regulators can be maintained in the cytoplasm and only transported into the nucleus at specific times in response to particular signals so that the response to those signals can be very rapid, not even being delayed long enough to read out the appropriate genes into mRNAs and having them assembled into newly minted proteins.

Another good reason seems to be to separate the transcription of the DNA into a mRNA from the process of translating that mRNA into the polypeptide chain it prescribes. In eukaryotic cells much of the nuclear DNA does not code for any proteins so it has been labeled "junk DNA" and assumed to be leftovers from the long evolutionary process of gearing up from smaller, simpler organisms that the cells simply have no way to get rid of. In the human genome it is estimated that only three percent of the DNA actually codes for proteins (although that still represents an estimated 100,000 protein-coding genes).

This non-coding DNA occurs within genes as well as between them. The wonder of eucaryotic cells is that these introns or interrupting segments of DNA are transcribed into the primary mRNA but then edited out and discarded before the mature mRNA is translated into the peptide chain of the protein. By separating the processes there is time for this editing of the mRNA to remove the introns before the peptide chain is assembled. In bacteria that have no nucleus and have no introns in their DNA the two processes go on almost simultaneously since all the molecular equipment is gathered together on the cell's outer and only membrane.

In some cases the editing of the mRNA before translation results in functionally distinct messengers produced from the same primary mRNA transcript. In humans the same gene read in the thyroid gland produces calcitonin but read in the hypothalamus of the brain produces the slightly different and functionally distinct calcitonin-gene-related-peptide (CGRP) because the tissue specific cells edit out different portions of the mRNA.

The early hints of the importance of non-protein coding DNA come from the identification of the regulatory sections of known genes. Each well-studied human gene has at least five such regulatory elements or segments, all DNA nucleotide sequences, and many are positioned outside the protein coding sequence. So a substantial amount of DNA is involved in such tasks.

We know that pseudogenes, defective DNA copies that lack the introns, are rarely expressed in cells. One mechanism proposed to explain that depends on study of the gene that shuts down one of the two X chromosomes in mammalian cells *without producing a protein* as far as the researchers can detect. It seems to do so with an RNA that sticks to the intron and blocks further activity in that area. In 1982 Thomas R. Cech and Sidney Altman discovered that some intron sequences in RNA have a built-in enzyme that lets them cut and splice together the exons themselves. They subsequently received the Nobel Prize for their work.

John Mattick, a molecular biologist at the University of Queensland in Australia, has proposed that the introns are a second regulatory mechanisms for the genes. He proposes that the virtual explosion of multicellular lifeforms that occurred 530 million years ago resulted from the evolution of this system (still not really understood by anyone let it be emphasized) that allowed the cells to regulate many more genes than the operon systems that we find in both procaryotic and eucaryotic cells (and discovered first in bacteria and quickly assumed to be the whole story) because they now have two systems of regulation, possibly separate and operating in very different ways. The total genetic library or *genome* of a plant or animal cell is much larger than that of any bacteria and it seems logical that some additional system would be needed to regulate that larger mass of chemical information. For plants the genome must be both complete and extensive because they need to be able to synthesize all of the amino acids and other essential molecule types since they have no reliable way to obtain them from outside as animals do from their food since plant foods are only inorganic minerals. We simply do not know how this intron system works and are waiting eagerly for someone to propose an analogy that can be tested experimentally. At the very least it is nicer to think that our genomes are not cluttered with 97 percent junk.

The evolving view is that each chromosome is a complex "information organelle" with sophisticated repair and control systems built right in among what seems to our unprepared eyes like meaningless junk.

It can be argued that the separation of the processes by a nuclear membrane is also a matter of efficiency. On a regular basis the cell is going to need specific proteins but it does not need each of them everywhere in the cell simultaneously. *Something* must travel from the DNA inside the nucleus to the ribosomes in order to have those protein molecules assembled. Since transportation costs are an important consideration in any system, and here they involve both the energy required to move the molecules in and out through the nuclear membrane plus that required to move the amino acid raw materials and then the finished proteins through everything else in the cytoplasm, then the fewer the molecules that must be moved any long distance, the more efficient the process.

With the existing system in all known eucaryotic cells only the signal molecules indicating what proteins are needed at that time and the mRNA molecules need to make the long trip into or out of the nucleus. The amino acids and the assembled proteins need only be moved to and from a ribosome close to where the protein will serve its purpose. And when we consider that a single mRNA molecule can act as template for the assembly of dozens or hundreds of molecules of a particular protein the savings in transport costs is much greater.

Particularly for digestive enzymes or other proteins that would be dangerous if loose within the cell it is important that the cell be able to assemble them by the endoplasmic reticulum or some other membrane enclosed space so that the peptide chain can penetrate through the membrane and only take on its functional three-dimensional shape where it is safely separated from the vital innards of the cell by a protective membrane.

In addition there is the space factor. Presumably the formation of a nuclear membrane made the early eucaryotic cells better able to survive because it reduced the problem of unwanted interactions between the DNA and various enzymes and other reactive molecules within the cell. Putting the DNA in a high security area with limited access avoids that. It therefore would defeat the purpose to have to move large numbers of many kinds of molecules in and out when they could do the job of protein assembly at least as well in the general cytoplasm. To do the job within the nucleus the ribosomes, the many kinds of transfer RNA (tRNA) molecules, amino acid molecules, and the ligase enzymes that hook the amino acids together, plus whatever "delivery trucks" are needed to move all of the movable ones of those would all have to be within the nuclear membrane churning and reacting while trying not to disturb the activities going on along the chromosomes. It is safer and easier to have them well separated.

The packaging of the DNA within the cell is a major physical feat since the molecules must be condensed by a factor of a thousand to fit within the nucleus. The trick is to fold or supercoil the helical molecule tightly but still leave room for the proteins that need to get access to those genes required in each cell type to reach the DNA. Supercoiling refers to coiling on a larger scale an already coiled strand.

At the smallest level the condensation is achieved by winding two loops of the DNA around histone proteins like thread around a spool and then packing these balls-on-a-string units into groups. There are typically five similar but slightly different forms of histones in a cell but these vary little between cell types. These wound-up segments are then folded into many accordion pleats and long segments fitted together somewhat like a knit sweater in which loops of yarn formed of many separate fibers are fitted into spaces between one another but not quite knitted together so that any section can be pulled out and then fitted back in again without having to unwind the whole length from the end as we would have to do with a knitted garment. There is some experimental evidence that folds of the DNA are literally pulled out of the condensed mass to be read or repaired and then neatly tucked back in.

Early on it was noted that in a test tube the histone proteins are acidophilic or acid-loving but in the cell they will not strongly attach acidic dyes unless the DNA has been chemically removed. This is a strong indication that the histones are actually bonded to the DNA. Further study concluded that the acidic dye cannot reach the histones because they are within the coils of the DNA, not adhering to the outside of it. Electron microscope pictures were eventually produced showing the balls-on-a-string configuration and the bits of information resolved.

Non-histone proteins, including actin and myosin the major molecular components of the animal muscle contraction system, are found in the nucleus and are suspected of being involved in the movement of molecules in and out of the organelle, of the movement of the nuclear contents during cell division, and possibly of some role in the maintenance or alteration of the nuclear structure as the cell contents thrash about as they do.

It is fundamental to understand that proteins work because of their shape. The peptide chain is the sequence of amino acids bonded together to form a continuous string but only when that is folded and cross-bonded into the 3-D shape that the size, shape, and charges of its amino acids require of it is the chain able to fit to other molecules and therefore be a functional molecule which is how we define a protein.

The simplicity of the genetic mechanism is that the sequence of nucleotide bases on the DNA and then the messenger RNA determines the sequence of amino acids in the peptide chain which in turn determines the 3-D shape of the protein and *that* is what determines what that protein type can do and the specific molecules to which it can fit and therefore react with.

A glitch in the terminology resulting from not knowing the details from the start is that some proteins require two or more separate peptide chains, each in its own 3-D shape, fitted together and cross-bonded together like a bent-nail puzzle (but not end to end so they always remain separate chains) to form a single functional molecule of the protein. In some cases then the single folded peptide chain is the protein but in other cases it is only part of the protein.

For reasons that are not clear having exactly the "correct" or normal amount of DNA within a cell is more critical to animals than to plants. In particular it is common to find plant types having whole extra sets of equivalent or homologous chromosomes, a condition called polyploidy since *ploid* refers to a single set of genes and therefore of non-equivalent chromosomes of the species. Some have as many as eight sets of homologous chromosomes. Such patterns are found in only a very few animal types though.

CHAPTER 8

THIS IS BASIC GENETICS IN ROSE

We all know from experience that seeds from rose plants produce more rose plants, not cabbages or cacti, and dogs have puppies not calves. Like begets like. Each species reproduces its own kind. But we have also observed that the rose plants and the puppies are not all exactly alike. There may be differences in size, shape, color, and the like. These are minor variations, individual differences, within the overall pattern of the species. Interestingly, both the similarity and the differences have the same basis -- genetics.

Genetics is the study of the patterns of inheritance of all living things. Any organism is the sum total of thousands and thousands of individual traits or characteristics, each of which is controlled by a sentence in the book of genetic instructions in the DNA of the cell. This sentence, the part of the genetic message that controls one particular trait, is called a gene. So we can conveniently say that we are all the end product of our genes. Biologists have understood that much for about a hundred years and we have learned a lot about inheritance and how to manipulate it to our own purposes. In the last thirty years or so they have been able to explain in much greater detail (although still not nearly completely) what that means at the level of the molecules that actually do what we can do.

Like everything else in living things, genetics begins in the cells. Every tiny cell in the body of every organism contains, coded in a special chemical way, the complete set of genetic instructions for the formation and the functioning of that particular type of organism. This means that the cells in the root of a rose bush contains all of the genetic instructions for the formation of flowers, the production of scent and nectar, and the making of chloroplasts to perform photosynthesis although the root will never be directly involved in any of these tasks.

This system, with its tremendous amount of extra duplication of material, makes sense once we recognize that this is the only practical way that a multicellular plant or animal could develop from a single cell, the fertilized egg or zygote, to maturity without great risk of disaster at every cell division during its entire development. If only the first cell of the multicellular plant contained all of the genetic information for the entire plant throughout its entire life cycle then at every cell division the genes must be sorted out and divided up so that each of the new cells formed will have all of the genes that it -- and all of the cells that will form from it later in the growth and development cycle -- will need to do all of their tasks. A monumental operation to say the least. And if at any cell division the wrong genes go into one of the two new cells formed then one or both of the resulting cells will be unable to carry out its assigned functions and the plant will suffer the consequences -- which would often be death. We would have to assume either this scenario or that the genes are somehow being created anew in each individual during its lifetime, which does not correspond to our observations of the growth and inheritance patterns of living things. And ultimately we would need to find out how all the genes get back together in the zygotes of each generation to start the whole business over again.

With a simple mechanism to give *every* cell a complete copy of the genetic message there is assurance that the cells that will reproduce the next generation will contain the instructions for making all of the body parts and all the cells formed during development will have access to all the genes they might need. This system also allows for the possibility of asexual or vegetative reproduction about which we will have more to say in **Chapter 14**.

Theoretically any cell from a multicellular organism could, under the right conditions, develop into a completely functioning mature member of its species since it has the complete set of inherited instructions for doing so. And in fact that is literally true these days. Especially with plants, but to even some extent with animals, this is done routinely in the process known as cloning. This process produces exact copies of the original organism from single cells or small pieces of tissue and is revolutionizing the ornamental plant industry by allowing mass production of plants that formerly were expensive and hard to find because they were slow or hard to propagate.

Our understanding of the patterns of inheritance dates back to about 1900. Gregor Mendel, an Austrian Augustinian monk, had done the foundation work on the subject and had published his discoveries and his explanation for them in 1866 but their significance was not appreciated at that time. Also, at that time no physical activity was known to occur inside cells that would explain how the changes that Mendel argued had to happen could actually occur.

It is only at the start of this century that a number of pieces of new information came together and several biologists rediscovered Mendel's paper and realized that he had the answer. In one of those marvelous bits of serendipity that sometimes happen in science, the Dutch researcher Hugo DeVries, the German Karl Correns, the Viennese Erick Tschermak, and the British William Bateson, working independently, all rediscovered Mendel's paper in the libraries and appreciated its importance within a matter of months.

Mendel deserves special credit for two insights from his basic research technique, little things that made a tremendous difference in making sense of what was being observed. First, he simply studied one inherited trait at a time, ignoring everything about the plants except the one feature he was studying in that experiment instead of trying to decipher the inheritance of all of the observable characteristics simultaneously. His famous experimental work was done with garden peas in the monastery garden. When he examined the plants and tried to observe and then predict what would happen if he cross-pollinated one with another he looked at only one trait at a time. He paid attention only to the height of the stem, or the color of the flower, or the color of the seed, not all of these things in the same group of experimental plants. Many other people of his day and before had gotten lost in the complexity of analyzing inheritance patterns because they tried to deal with too many features at once. Following Mendel's lead we still today initially analyze each trait separately. It seems like such a simple thing, but it made such a big difference. Mendel's published paper examined seven different traits in pea plants, each studied and analyzed separately. Once we understand the inheritance pattern of each separate trait then we can set up experiments in which we can predict and analyze the inheritance of a small number of traits simultaneously. We can study any number of traits at once but the analysis of more than four or five gets too complicated to be useful.

Mendel's second big contribution was the mathematical analysis of his data. Today we would be surprised to find scientists approaching a problem in any other way but in Mendels day biological problems were not generally considered to be subjects for mathematical analysis. With the widespread use of statistics today to make sense of mountains of complex data we may lose sight of how difficult it may be to see patterns in data without such techniques.

Consider the situation as Mendel himself faced it. He had examined seven characteristics in the peas for each of which he could recognize two forms. In each case he had started out with parent plants that, if allowed to self pollinate as peas normally do, would always produce only offspring with the same form of the trait as the parent. These are what became known as *true breeding lines*. Today we would call them homozygous for that trait. He cross-pollinated plants showing the two different forms of the trait he was interested in, such as flower color or position of flowers. When he grew the seeds of this mating the next season he noted that all of the offspring showed only one of the two forms of the trait that had been seen in the parents. He then cross-pollinated these offspring and saved their seeds for the next year. When he grew these third generation plants (what we would call the second filial or F2 generation, the "grandchildren") he found both forms of each trait were observable again, but in unequal proportions. Now he had to try to make sense of this. Mendel's published data for the F2 generations looked like this:

Round seed	vs.	Wrinkled seed	5474	round;	1850	wrinkled
Yellow seed	vs.	Green seed	6022	yellow;	2001	green
Gray seed coat	vs.	White seed coat	705	gray;	224	white
Inflated pods	vs.	Wrinkled pods	882	inflated	299	wrinkled
Green pod color	vs.	yellow pod	428	green;	152	yellow
Axial flowers	vs.	terminal flowers	651	axial;	207	terminal
Long stem	vs.	short stem	787	long;	227	short

Can you see a pattern or relationship which holds for all of these different traits in those numbers? Few people could. But by the simple mathematical step of taking a *ratio* of the numbers of the two forms of each trait no matter what the actual numbers are, the analysis becomes much simpler because the pattern becomes fairly obvious. Look at Mendel's data again as his training in mathematics and physics gave him the insight to do.

Round seed	vs.	Wrinkled seed	2.96	round:	1	wrinkled
Yellow seed	vs.	Green seed	3.01	yellow:	1	green
Gray seed coat	vs.	White seed coat	3.15	gray:	1	white
Inflated pods	vs.	Wrinkled pods	2.95	inflated	1	wrinkled
Green pod color	vs.	yellow pod	2.82	green;	1	yellow
Axial flowers	vs.	terminal flowers	3.14	axial;	1	terminal
Long stem	vs.	short stem	2.84	long;	1	short

For each of the different traits the ratio of the two forms in the F2 generation experimental plants closely approximated three to one. So there must be a basic, and presumably universal, mechanism controlling the inheritance of all of these separate traits. From this data Gregor Mendel drew several conclusions that have come to be known as his Principles of Inheritance.

First, there must be distinct physical structures in the cell which control the inheritance and which get passed from one generation to the next. This is the basis of our modern gene theory, although Mendel himself did not use that name. He wrote of what we call genes today as "inheritable units". He postulated that they must exist in order to explain the inheritance patterns that he observed but neither he nor anybody else in the 1800s had any idea where in the cell they might be located. Today we know what they are and where they are.

Second, he concluded that those inheritable units must occur in pairs and when the cell divides to form gametes or reproductive cells (pollen or sperm and eggs) only one of each pair of genes goes into each reproductive cell. That is, for each trait there must to be two genes in the normal cells. These may be genes for different forms of the trait, so a pea plant might have a gene for red flowers and a gene for white flowers. When that pea plant makes flowers each of its pollen cells and egg cells gets either the gene for red flowers or the gene for white flowers, but not both. This has become known as *Mendel's Principle of Segregation of Characters.*

Since each gamete contains one gene for each trait of the species, when the pollen and egg cells fuse in fertilization and become one cell that cell, the first cell of the new multicellular organism, has pairs of genes for all of the traits again. It is a beautifully simple mechanism for making sure that in each generation the genetic characteristics get mixed around to produce new combinations without burdening each new generation with more and more gene units within the cells.

Mendel also concluded that when each pair of inheritable units separated to form gametes (in what we now know as the process of cell division called meiosis) it did so independent of how any other pair separated. That is, all of the genes from the pollen parent would not automatically go into the same new gamete. The splitting of each pair was a separate roll of the dice and all, of the possible chance combinations of the forms would occur with equal frequency. This has become known as the *Principle of Independent Assortment*.

We have to make a significant correction or clarification to Mendel's statement on this point and then it will correspond to our current understanding of genetics. Mendel assumed, since he did not know what cell structures were the actual inheritable units, that each gene was a separate physical entity. We now know that each gene is a section of a DNA molecule in the nucleus of the cell that contains the coded instructions for prescribing a single protein. Therefore a single chromosomes has hundreds or even thousands of genes along its length. We can now demonstrate experimentally that individual genes do not assort independently but that the chromosomes, each a continuous DNA molecule, do. So if we alter Mendel's statement to say that each pair of *chromosomes* assorts independently the statement if valid.

Independent assortment means that the gametes of an individual may contain any combination of the different gene forms present in it that are located on separate chromosomes. Let us consider as an example a petunia plant that inherited genes for pink flower color (P), small flower size (l) and upright stem growth pattern (s) from its pollen parent and genes for white flower color (r), large flower size (L), and sprawling stem growth pattern (S) from its egg parent. We can then represent the genes for these traits present in this plant as PpLlSs. When this plant now forms pollen and egg cells the pairs of genes, represented by the different letters, are separated and only one of each goes into each gamete cell. If the gene for pink flowers (P) goes into a call it has no influence on the other pairs of genes that are located on separate chromosomes. Which of the genes for flower size goes into that gamete is a matter of chance. And which of the stem growth pattern genes goes into that gamete is a separate chance event. The mathematical laws of chance and many breeding experiments over the years all indicate that the separation of each pair of chromosomes is a separate chance event and all of the possible chance combinations will occur with equal frequency. From our example petunia plant we will get each of the gene combinations PLS, PLs. P1S, Pls, pLS, pLs, plS, pls in approximately one-eighth of the gametes.

One of the genetic realities which can complicate our prediction of the results of breeding particular plants together and our ability to manipulate the genes by normal breeding methods to obtain the most desirable combinations of genes is the fact that genes on the same chromosomes are inherited as a package deal. These genes are called *linked* because they are located together as parts of the same DNA molecule. Linked genes do not get randomly assorted from one another during meiosis.

Mendel's last point is the most readily observed one and was actually the one that led him to the others. This is the *Principle of Dominance*. It describes and explains the most common and basic inheritance pattern.

In many traits in any species there are two or more different forms of the trait that are the result of different forms of the same gene that are located at corresponding locations on the pair of related chromosomes of the individuals. These different forms of the same trait are called allelic genes or alleles. Often when genes for two different allelic forms of a trait are present in the same individual only one of the forms can be observed. This is the *dominant* allelic form. The form that gets covered over by the other is the *recessive* allelic form.

Mendel came to his conclusions about how inheritance had to work by noting that if he crossbred parents from true breeding lines of two different allelic forms (for example a pea plant from a population that always produced 100% red flowered plants if allowed to self-pollinate and a pea plant from a population that always produced 100% white flowered plants if allowed to self-pollinate) every one of their offspring had red flowers. The white flower trait had disappeared. If he now crossbred the members of this population of offspring (which we call the first filial or F1 generation) among themselves one fourth of the offspring in the next generation would have white flowers. So he concluded that the white flower trait had not been destroyed, only covered over and hidden by the red flower color. This forced him to conclude that the gene for white flower color could be present in a plant that showed red flowers and the only way that could happen was if there were two flower color genes in each plant.

This conclusion was supported by the observation that if the red flowered plants of the F2 generation were then allowed to self-pollinate only one-third of them (one fourth of the whole F2 generation) would produce exclusively red flowered offspring. The others, one-half of the original F2 generation, would produce both red and white flowered offspring in predictable proportions so we call them *heterozygous* or "having different kinds of zygotes".

Our grasp of the patterns of inheritance has allowed us to "design" new plants in a deliberate way through controlled breeding and has resulted in many improved food, forage, and ornamental crops in the minimum time because there is a lot less trail-and-error involved in the choice of breeding stock. We have at the same time gained an appreciation for the complexity of the many traits controlled by several separate sets of genes and of the genetic control processes so we do not have unrealistically optimistic expectations about how much we can shape the organisms to meet our plans or how fast we can change whole plant populations.

Understanding the simplest pattern of genetic dominance allowed researchers to explain most of the more complicated ones because they are all variations on the same mechanisms described by Mendel in his principles. Genetic engineering promises a new era of plant science. It is a new way of manipulating the genes based on their molecular structure, not a new idea about how genetics works, and especially not anything that contradicts Mendel's observations or that makes them obsolete.

One major update is that we now know that there are DNA segments that we call *transposons* or "jumping genes" that can remove themselves from one chromosome and insert themselves into a different one, producing changes in the genetic nature of the individual if they disrupt or alter genes or their controls at the spot where they plug themselves in.

The Rosa *canina* aggregation is a group that the taxonomists and the geneticists get headaches trying to sort out. Most of the dog roses are polyploids with chromosome numbers ranging from 28 in the tetraploids to 42 in the hexaploids with most having 35. There is an unequal synapsis in the meiosis to form both the male and female gametes. Seven chromosomes segregate normally and these always end up in one daughter nucleus at Telophase I while the remaining 14 to 28, depending on the plant, go into the other daughter cell. Subsequently the male gametes containing the seven chromosomes mature but those with the other chromosomes abort. In the female gametes the cells with the seven chromosomes always abort. Leaving a cell with the unmixed chromosomes to become the egg (which will have 21 to 35 chromosomes). The egg cells effectively have maternal inheritance of an unaltered package of genes despite being formed by meisosis. Fertilization produces embryos with from 28 to 42 chromosomes and endosperm that has a very unusual 6-12:1 female to male ratio of chromosomes.

This is a type of facultative agamospermy or "seeds without sex" but it still needs fertilization so it is distinct from apomixis. Sexual and asexual reproduction by seed coexist in this group of roses. What seems to be unique to *Rosa canina* is that features of both reproductive methods coexist in every meiosis -- the seven pairs of chromosomes donated by the pollen parent get mixed while the remaining genes that are always contributed by the female parent are conserved unchanged.

CHAPTER 9

THESE ARE ROSE'S HYBRIDS

Somewhere back in the pre-historic period our ancestors began to save seeds from species like peas and deliberately planted them where they could be protected while they produced a food crop the next year. In the seven thousand or so years since then we also learned to select the best plants and save their seeds to plant for the next crop, and then to pick the best parents to cross pollinate to produce superior offspring for the future. It was trial-and-error without much of a basis in theory but over long periods it paid off in domesticated crops that gave much higher yields than their wild counterparts and also played the farmer's game by doing things like having the grains stay on the stem until they are harvested as a group rather than falling off early and being scattered by the wind or eaten by the small animals on the ground.

At some point in early agriculture people learned to try to combine the best traits of different forms of a crop species or its relatives into a single type, a hybrid or mongrel type that would be the logical best choice as the type to grow. With no good understanding of the basics of genetics and a lot of input from superstition and experts who knew nothing of value this work probably failed more often than it succeeded for a variety of reasons that we can only now explain in biological terms. It succeeded often enough though to allow what we describe as civilization to develop as hunter-gatherer groups became settled farmers and eventually the agricultural yields would allow some people to do other things so that cities, trading, and armies could spring up.

Hybrid forms were produced from early times but they were only a minor improvement because the parents used were highly heterozygous and therefore there was a wide range of combinations of desirable and less desirable traits among them. This means that initially the majority of the offspring from any cross were likely to be no more desirable than either parent and many would be distinctly less so. But there were always the few that could be carefully selected out that *were* superior and if only these were used as parents of the next seed crop then each year the average value of the offspring would increase and a somewhat larger percentage of them would be superior. But it took many years to produce much difference and few farmers had the skill and the patience to search out the few slightly better plants in a whole field and carefully save their seed to plant the next season rather than stew all but a randomly selected sackful up with a bit of roast beast.

A big advantage of hybrids is that they can represent a kind of genetic cheating. In genetic dominance one form of a particular gene can effectively hide the expression of one or more other forms of that same gene. We now understand that this is a matter of the *dominant* allelic form making the completely effective protein called for by the trait while the *recessive* form(s) produce slightly different and often somewhat less efficient or even outright defective types of the protein.

To use a hypothetical and simplified but not unrealistic example, if the completely dominant gene produces a red pigment in the flower petals then any plant with that allele will have red flowers. And this is the critical point -- the flowers of the heterozygous plants will be just as red as those of their homozygous siblings. In practical terms this means that if a parent plant is homozygous for some desirable traits all of its offspring will have those traits no matter what gene pattern the second parent has. It also means that if the plant you want to use as parent because of other traits is homozygous for some undesirable ones there is no way to avoid the fact that all the young will have those bad genes.

Even if the hybrids have some less desirable genes hidden away so they would not be good breeding stock themselves it is a lot easier to breed up parent lines each of which has some desirable traits in homozygous form to use as parents of offspring that will give you a crop with all those good traits.

Garden roses have complicated genealogies, often involving several species and many hybrid varieties. Several major groups of hybrids have been produced over the centuries and they often contributed particular groups of traits to our modern forms. Since there are about 200 species of wild roses surviving worldwide the process will undoubtedly continue for a long time yet. A good example is yellow flower color which was introduced into hybrids from the Chinese *Rosa foetida*. French grower Joseph Pernet-Ducher spent 13 years cross breeding to produce a decent yellow, the variety 'Persian Yellow', and another 12 years (until 1898) to produce a pure yellow garden rose 'Rayon d'or'.

The China rose has been in cultivation about 5000 years. The Gallica rose is the oldest European species known to have been in cultivation. Reliable records mention it being grown in the first century A.D. Rosa *damascene bifera* was the first of the fall repeat bloomers among the damask roses. *Rosa rugosa* may contribute resistance to black spot disease (caused by the fungus *Diplocarpon rosea)* to hybrids but since there is evolution going on that will not last long before more aggressive pathogen strains show up.

Hybrid teas first appeared in 1867 as crosses between hybrid perpetuals and tea roses (that get that name from the scent which reminded people of the smell of the chests used to ship tea from the Orient). Hybrid perpetuals are the most complex hybrids, counting China, Bourbon, Portland, and Noisette types among their ancestors. The perpetual varieties were big Victorian favorites because, as the name suggests, they bloomed over a long season. The Victorians developed some 1000 varieties of which about 100 are still being grown today.

The Noisette types were first produced by a South Caroline planter who crossed the musk rose with the China rose. These were subsequently developed and made famous by the French grower Noisette whose name stuck with them. The polyanthas were derived from the China rose crossed with the Asian *R. multiflora*. Later the floribundas with large clusters of blooms resulted from crosses between polyanthas and hybrid teas. The first of the floribundas were produced in Holland in 1911.

Not too many years ago if you planted a packet of flower or vegetable seeds you got a variety of colors, sizes and shapes. They were all the species you had planted but they were far from uniform. They reflected the normal variation in many traits among a diverse group of parental plants. This made it difficult to plan a color scheme for your plantings or to assure that your vegetables would mature at close enough to the same time to make canning easy, but it was the best we could do. But we've come a long way in genetics in recent years.

These days we routinely turn out large numbers of seeds of particular varieties that will produce almost identical plants. You can buy a packet of seeds that will give you red flowered plants, twelve inches tall for the front of the house and another packet of the same species that will give you white flowered plants six inches tall for the backyard. Your tomatoes, onions, and cabbages will be as alike as the proverbial peas in a pod. For commercial growers in particular, having many acres of a crop mature simultaneously so they can be machine harvested all at one time is extremely important.

These marvels of modern breeding are Fl hybrids, the first *filial* or offspring generation from selected parents. The terminology was coined by W. Bateson early in this century. These are plants and animals that are revolutionizing our agriculture and facilitating our biological research efforts. They result from the crossing of two carefully selected inbred parent lines, each a number of individuals that have been bred and selected to be homozygous, to have their two genes for each of their many traits the same allelic form and therefore all the members of each type are virtually the same. When the two parental lines are crossed we can produce large numbers of offspring simultaneously that are all identical because each receives the same group of genes from each parent line. Yet these offspring, the Fl, are all heterozygous because each has two different forms of the gene for many of its traits, one form inherited from each parent. Since the Fl all inherit the same pattern of genes they are practically identical, with most of the small differences between them the result of the environment rather than their genes.

The Fl hybrids have several major advantages over random bred forms. First, by careful selection of the parent types many of the advantageous characteristics can be controlled by dominant forms of genes -- thus assuring that the dominant form of the trait will appear in all the offspring. Second, but most important to the breeder, the developer of the hybrid strain can retain exclusive control of its production by controlling access to those parental strains. And third, they often show what is called *heterosia* or hybrid vigor.

In 1952 Thaddeus Dobzhansky pointed out that heterosis could produce either hybrid luxuriance in which they grew faster or larger, etc. without actually being any better adapted to the environment or they could have superior adaptive fitness so they could do well under a greater variety of local conditions than the parent types even if they were only standard size. Often they show some of each advantage.

Hybrid luxuriance is an observed tendency of heterozygous individuals in many species to have more vigorous growth. In plants that takes the form of more and larger flowers, more seeds, earlier germination, greater disease resistance, and higher crop yields. Farmers long ago noted this and geneticists (once there were such since the science of genetics is effectively limited to this century) confirmed that hybrid vigor is a general phenomenon. Hybrids or individuals of mixed stock tend to be a bit more of whatever we as the manipulators of types are looking for. Mules are stronger that their horse parent and more amenable than their donkey parent. Hybrid corn yields more tons of grain per acre than either of the parent strains it came from. Hybrid snapdragons produce more and larger flowers.

We have only speculation backed by suggestive observations to explain hybrid vigor but the reality exists even if we are less than certain of the mechanisms. One likely factor is that the hybrid gets the best of both parents - it inherits the genetically dominant alleles that cover over some of its less desirable recessive ones. It is also possible that in some way we have not yet grasped being heterozygous, literally having more kinds of genes for many traits, affects the genetic control systems and allows these hybrid individuals to do things better. This could be due to the hybrids having greater biochemical versatility or because there is some synergistic interaction between the gene products of the two alleles that gives the combination extra impact (a phenomenon called overdominance) or because of some synergism or interaction between one of the allele's product and that from some other gene that affects the overall effect (this phenomenon called epistasis).

The whole F1 hybrid production process starts with the development of inbred varieties with highly desirable traits to be used as the parent types. These are bred only within their own group for many generations to sort out the differences and produce homozygous inbred lines. Initially the animals or plants that are selected have many genes that are different. When their young (the second generation) are bred among themselves some of *their young* (the third generation) will inherit the same form of the gene from each parent. These individuals are now homozygous for that gene. By selecting only those in each generation that come closest to the ideal form originally intended as parent for the next group we can eventually produce a group that are statistically likely to be genetically identical. With each generation of such inbreeding relatives the number of genes that come together in homozygous form increases. Along the way many weak, sterile, and aberrant forms are weeded out by the selection process. The resulting plants will all be alike generation after generation as long as they are only breed within this group.

The inbred types are the equivalent of clones except that they were produced by sexual rather than asexual reproduction. In 1922 Sewell Wright calculated that the statistical likelihood that members of a population are homozygous for any and all genes approaches 98% after twenty generations of the equivalent of brother-sister matings. For new types being produced as offshoots of established inbred strains this degree of statistical assurance may be reached in even fewer generations. The statistical calculations are the basis of all our inbreeding work in agriculture and research to do things like establish homozygous parental lines.

Inbred lines are uniform and highly predictable. A great deal of hard-nosed selection over years of careful work goes into producing a successful Fl introduction. To develop a new Fl hybrid line a number of promising inbred lines are mated in different combinations and the offspring of each pairing are evaluated separately. When and if a particularly desirable pattern is found a new commercial Fl hybrid is likely to result. The vast majority of crosses that are tested are worthless.

Often the hybrids from the reciprocal crosses -- using strain A as the male parent in one case and as the female parent in the other -- are strikingly different and one may be valuable and the other useless. Sometimes it matters who is on top. In such cases it is highly desirable to produce either male sterile or female sterile strains. These are a plant breeder's dream because they allow large scale field production of Fl hybrid seed with minimal difficulty. In most cases it is only male sterile forms that have allowed commercial production of Fl crop species like onions. These produce normal eggs and fruit but are not able to make functional pollen cells. The male sterile plants can then be used as the female or egg parents for the desired hybrids by interplanting rows of the male sterile and pollen-producing strains and harvesting only the seed of the male steriles as the Fl hybrids. In Marigolds *(Tagetes* species) a mutation for apetaly in which the flower heads produce no petals and look like shaving brushes is linked to male sterility so these flowers also produce no pollen. These are ideal female parents for crosses to produce Fl hybrid seed in the popular ornamentals.

Once the desirable parental combination has been determined the breeder must mass produce the parental types, keeping each genetically isolated and pure. From these he can then start to mass produce the Fl hybrids for sale as seed or started plants. His task is complicated and expensive since every year he must now grow and protect the genetic purity of three strains -- the two inbred parent strains and the cross between them. It is this process, added on top of the years of work developing the inbred lines and screening all the crosses between them with no assurance of any ultimate success, that explains and justifies the high cost of Fl hybrids.

The production of Fl plant hybrids involves different problems than breeding domesticated animals. Plant Fls have come in several waves. The first were the species in which homozygous parental types had already been developed. These were mainly species that could be raised in screened-in greenhouses to prevent uncontrolled pollination by insects and could be efficiently hand pollinated. This is a tedious but sometimes necessary task in which the flower's own pollen producing anthers are removed before they mature so they cannot release any pollen, and later carefully selected pollen is applied to the mature and receptive female flower part, the pistil, with a paintbrush or an "electric finger", a small vibrating device that fits on the end of a finger and sprinkles pollen uniformly. This task puts whole cadres of young adults through college by providing summer jobs. Such an approach is economically feasible on a commercial scale only for plants like petunias and tomatoes where a large number of seeds will result from each pollination. Even under these conditions a new cultivated variety can take as much as nine years to become commercially available.

For the tiny seeds of petunias a large amount of expensive hand labor goes into producing the few ounces of seed of a particular Fl each year. However, those few ounces of seed are worth many thousands of dollars when divided up into packets that each contain a tiny fraction of an ounce of seed -- which is still usually 35-150 seeds, depending on variety and company, more than most people have room for. In the case of corn where the separate male tassel and female silk flower clusters on the plants make it feasible and the increased yields from the hybrids makes the costs worthwhile, hand detasseling of the female parent strain in the field is done.

A second wave of Fls resulted from the discovery of self incompatibility, a genetic mechanism that keeps some species from self-pollinating under normal circumstances. In some species the pollen gamete cannot develop and fertilize an egg in a flower containing the same form of a special self-incompatibility gene that it contains. In other cases the process is more complicated because it depends on the genetic dominance of the forms of the self-incompatibility gene. In these cases pollen of a genetically dominant allelic form can fertilize a flower but one with a recessive allele will be inhibited. Carefully selected parental strains with compatible genes for this trait can be insect pollinated in the field and the seed will all be hybrid because the self-pollinated flowers simply cannot set seed.

In other plants the pattern of a group of different or nonallelic pairs of genes, not a single gene pair, determines the outcome of pollination for a particular trait and there may be a gradation or series of slightly different forms between the extreme forms. Such a highly variable trait is said to be controlled by multiple alleles. Many grain and other agricultural crops involve such complicated patterns and require the mathematical analysis of population genetics to select strains for improvement.

Sometimes the selection for the hybrids occurs at the seedling stage. For instance, to produce commercial seed, celery is pollinated by blowflies placed in a muslin sleeve around the female parent flower stalk with a male flower stalk that has been cut off and placed in a tube of water in there. If light green female and dark green male parents are used, then when the seeds sprout all the dark green seedlings are hybrids but any light green ones are the result of self-pollination and are discarded.

The production of hybrids is not always easy of course. In 1963 Dr. O. Hayose reported in the *Japanese Journal* of *Breedina* that a cross between pumpkin *(Cucurbita moschata)* and squash *(C. pepo)* was most successful if the pumpkin was used as the female parent and it was pollinated at 7 a.m. with pollen from the squash which had been collected at 10 p.m. the previous night and stored at 10°C. The reciprocal cross (pumpkin as pollen parent) was only successful if made at 4 a.m.

Genetic engineering is in its infancy but it holds out tantalizing prospects. In theory we will be able to sort through a species genome and replace specific mutant genes that we consider to be defective with corrected copies or even just correct the DNA sequence of the gene as it sits in the chromosome. That is what we are particularly interested in doing in cases of human genetic based diseases. The real prospect of genetic engineering however is the ability to add specific traits to the repertoire of what a species can do by transferring the functional genes that permit it from some other species -- and we are not limited to other plant species, let along only close relatives. The prospect of making plants that gather nitrogen fertilizer from the air -- with or without the aid of bacteria living symbiotically within their roots, crops that make higher protein meals, and rapidly growing trees with wood that contains little lignin so it can be easily made into paper has the labs working overtime and Wall Street panting with anticipation.

Some practical applications are already realized, like trees that synthesize their own insecticide using a bacterial gene. And a team has successfully transferred a flower development gene from a rapid growing small plant into European aspen trees which causes them to make flowers their first year rather than taking the ten to twenty years this is normal. This technique should speed the production of hybrid trees that have always been a problem because of the decades it takes to grow up each generation so they can be crossbred to make the next improved group.

CHAPTER 10

THESE ARE ROSE'S MITOCHONDRIA

Rose needs energy to make many of her metabolic reactions go and to get that energy she oxidizes or burns the same kinds of fuel molecules that we do. And like us she does most of the job of releasing that energy within special organelles called mitochondria (singular = mitochondrion) that are found in the cytoplasm of each of her cells. Bacteria that require oxygen depend on the same chemical reactions even if they are not concentrated in a discrete membrane-enclosed unit.

The mitochondria are the sites of most reactions of aerobic cell respiration, the multistep process that breaks down fuel molecules to release energy so it can be delivered everywhere in the cell by ATP transfer molecules. Glucose and fatty acid molecules are apparently the only fuels the system can handle. Any other useful types are chemically converted into these or their partial decomposition products in order to fit into the molecular machinery.

Mitochondria were first seen in muscle cells by A. Kolleker in 1857. He described his isolation of some for better study in 1888. In 1890 German cytologist R. Altmann developed a staining technique that lets us see them in living cells. He reported that they were enclosed in their own wrapping and were not connected to any other cell parts and he seems to have been the first to suggest that they were autonomous organisms living within the cytoplasm of host cells.

The mitochondria provided some of the first evidence that metabolic functions might be localized in specific organelles. In 1912 B.F. Kingsbury suggested they might be the site of cellular respiration but it was not until the 1950s that they were generally recognized as both the site of cell respiration and the source of nearly all of the ATP in aerobic cells. They were described early on as the *powerhouses* of the cell.

Energy must be released from fuel molecules both in small enough doses not to damage the cell and under circumstances that allow part of it to be captured to form molecular bonds. Only then can it be transferred within those molecules to where it is needed and only released precisely when it is needed-

Adenosine triphosphate (ATP) molecules are the universal energy currency of cells. Every cell type studied, from bacteria to man, uses this small molecule type to taxi energy from where it is available in a cell (mostly the mitochondria) to wherever it is needed to make various chemical reactions go. The ATP transports the energy within its chemical bonds but the molecule itself does not get involved in the reactions that require the energy. It is difficult to get a good analogy for this because inevitably we want to compare the energy to some structure, some matter, and that is precisely what it is not.

The beauty of the energy transfer system is that its molecular parts are reusable so that only the energy gets used up and needs to be continually replaced. The basic molecule is adenosine monophosphate (AMP) which is also an RNA nucleotide, one of the combination sugar-phosphate-base units that get fitted into long chains that are the RNA molecules. A molecule of adenine is bonded to one carbon of a five-carbon ribose sugar molecule that has a phosphate unit ($PO4^{-3}$) attached to another of its carbons. In an RNA molecule the sugar and phosphate groups form the backbone while the adenine is the genetic code element. For energy transfer uses, one or two additional phosphates (referred to as inorganic phosphate groups or Pi) are attached to the first one. When the second phosphate is attached the molecule becomes adenosine diphosphate (ADP). The third makes it ATP.

It takes energy to form those bonds between the phosphate units but that energy is released when the bonds are later broken. And that is the basis of the system. In the mitochondrion an ADP adds Pi and energy and becomes ATP. The ATP is then moved to a spot in the cell where energy is needed. Here it is split apart to become ADP and Pi, releasing the energy which is taken up by the reaction that needs it. The ADP and Pi are then moved back to one of the mitochondria to join the stockpile of parts ready to be used again and again.

In the last fifty years a string of studies have laid out for us the details of the enzyme sequences and molecular mechanisms by which energy is released from fuel molecules in the mitochondria. That is spelled out in detail in today's textbooks. The bottom line is that the energy is released in the form of high energy electrons and those enter an electron transport chain where they move from one protein to another releasing their excess energy in small doses that can be used by some of the proteins to bond ADP and Pi to form ATP molecules. The electron transport chain is somewhat like water falling down the series of small steps of a fish ladder and losing some of its energy at each level rather than spilling over the top of the dam to fall the entire height and vigorously scour out the river below.

The last step in this operation requires oxygen atoms to combine with hydrogen atoms coming out of the chain and form water molecules. This is the reason that all of us that have to breathe oxygen need it -- to remove those hydrogen atoms that will otherwise back up through the chain and stop the whole process. The oxygen keeps the energy release process going by making water. Without that we would soon be dead.

Mitochondria vary in size but usually are about five percent of the size of the nucleus. They are barely visible with the light microscope with special staining but are easily seen with the transmission electron microscope. In time lapse films they turn, twist, and move around in the cell. They can also fuse together or divide into separate units.

Together an average of 1700 mitochondria per cell represent about 39% of the total cell internal membrane surface and 22% of the total volume in the liver cells that are considered to be typical animal cells. Those figures are probably somewhat smaller for plant cells because those do less mechanical work. Their number in the cells of a tissue type reflects the amount of physical work that tissue performs. Fat cells have few mitochondria but sperm and muscle cells have a great many. The mitochondria of plant cells are less regular in size and structure than those of animal cells.

There is some evidence to suggest that in many cell types there is only one or a small number of separate mitochondria that are large and have complex branched shapes so that in the electron microscope pictures, which are of cells cut to expose their interiors, we get the false impression of many separate structures. However other studies on intact living cells do seem to find multiple structures. All of which simply emphasizes the real life dynamism of these organelles.

What advantages might there be to having a number of small units rather than one big mitochondrion? They can be concentrated where they are needed within the cell. They can multiply or be destroyed when appropriate to match the cell's energy needs without causing an interruption in the function. Since they move and change shape within the cell accidents can happen so there is safety in numbers. And with large enough numbers random sorting during cell division almost guarantees each new cell some.

Mitochondria are bounded by two double-layered or unit membranes with the inner shaped into folds called *cristae*. Those folds increase the surface area for this most critical chemical activity and take full advantage of the enclosed space without increasing the volume of the cells. This is similar to the structure of the interior of the chloroplast. Elaborately folded membranes in both set up local conditions that allow the special chemistry to occur. The cristae may be shaped as shelves, tubes, or more complex 3-D shapes. The significance of that is not known. The number of cristae varies with the demand for ATPs.

The composition of the outer membrane is unexceptional but the inner one contains about 70% protein and 30% lipids. These lipids include very little cholesterol but about 40% are lecithins and 15% are a phospholipid called cardiolipin that is synthesized at the outer membrane and that seems to be found in no other eucaryotic membranes although it is found in the membranes of some bacteria.

The inner membrane surface has many thousands of respiratory assemblies embedded in it, each containing a complete set of the molecule types necessary to conduct the process of ATP formation by way of the electron transport chain. This membrane is much more selective about what passes through it than is the outer one. There are specific carrier systems in it to get the fuel molecule types in and the end products out. One carrier specifically swaps an ATP from inside for an ADP from outside.

The inner membrane is surrounded on both sides by a liquid matrix. This matrix is almost a gel since it contains 50% protein. The enzymes needed to cut up the carbon chains of fuel molecules in the citric acid cycle to form carbon dioxide, water, and the high energy electrons that enter the electron transport chain are all here in the fluid-filled space along with the DNA, RNAs and ribosomes of the organelle. This concentrated soup keeps the essential functions running at high speed since the fuel molecules will quickly encounter the appropriate enzymes.

Plant mitochondrial DNA is circular and the genome is 140 times as long as in human cells but it is still at most half the length of a typical bacterial genome. The size of the organelle genomes also varies greatly among related species. Mitochondria replicate their own DNA, it does not have to go to the nucleus to be copied. This DNA contains no interrupting segments or introns so all the messenger, ribosomal, and transfer RNAs are transcribed as continuous strands that must then be cut into the proper pieces by an endonuclease enzyme made in the nucleus in order- to release the separate molecules.

A major physical difference that requires a different mindset to deal with is that, ignoring polyploids for the moment, each eucaryotic cells has only one or two copies of each nuclear gene but that same cell will have from a hundred to as many as ten thousand molecules of either chloroplast or mitochondrion DNA, each containing the entire genome of that organelle. So there are large *populations* of organelle chromosomes affecting the cell and it requires the mathematical analysis of population genetics to make sense of the inheritance implications. That topic goes beyond our consideration here but indicates that we can not think of all gene-controlled matters in the same way.

Mitochondrial (and chloroplast) ribosomes are notably different from those in the cytoplasm of the eucaryotic cell and much like those in bacteria. They are inhibited by antibiotics like chloramphenicol that prevent protein synthesis in bacteria but are not affected by compounds like cycloheximide that inhibit cytoplasmic ribosomes of the cell the mitochondria are in.

The mitochondrion's ribosomal RNAs are coded in its own genome but, depending on the species, all or most of the essential proteins that form parts of those ribosomes are coded in the nucleus and are actually made in the cytoplasm and moved intact into the mitochotidrion. As many as 200 nuclear genes seem to influence the synthesis of mitochondrial components.

Flowering plants have three distinct types of ribosomal or rRNA while yeast and mammals have only two. The third rRNA is similar to one of the small parts of their cytoplasmic rRNA but does not seem to have a counterpart in the yeast or mammal cells.

The genetic code in the mitochondrion differs from that in bacteria as well as from that of the otherwise universal code used by the genes in the nucleus. And it is not quite the same in the mitochondria of all kinds of eucaryotic cells. Typically it has four base triplets (UGA, AUA, CUA and AGA) that code for different amino acids or signals in these organelles.

There are only 22 types of transfer or tRNA types in the mitochondrion, fewer than the minimum number of types predicted to be needed to code for all the amino acids and signals. It seems that in this organelle only the first two of the three-letter gene code are used to prescribe what is inserted into the polypeptide chain being formed. This lack of specificity for the third base is not seen in the cytoplasmic ribosome system.

New mitochondria seem to always arise as a result of the growth and division of pre-existing ones or from specialized small structures that are effectively undeveloped organelles.

Mitochondria and chloroplasts are the opposite ends of a continuous energy exchange system with the non-living world. Both have double membrane systems with complex internal membrane structures. Both grow and divide independent of the rest of the cell. Both produce ATP in similar ways. Both have their own DNA, RNA, and ribosomes. All of which suggests that the *Endosymbiont Hypothesis* which proposes that both these and other cell parts originated as independent bacteria-like cells that entered and became essential parts of the early eucaryotic cells. The biochemical evidence seems substantial enough to support this as a useful hypothesis even though it does not prove it.

Surely a symbiotic event like the incorporation of either a photosynthetic machine or an efficient energy converter like a mitochondrion-type unit would have given early cells a distinct survival advantage. We would expect the combination of the two independent symbiotic events would have given the new eucaryotic cells such an advantage that they could almost totally outcompete all other cell types except in localized and limiting conditions.

In 1983 C. William Birky, Jr. suggested in *Science* that if the mitochondria and chloroplasts entered early eucaryotic cells as procaryotic "guest workers", natural selection would have favored those genomes that produced multiple copies so that one or more would end up in each daughter cell at each mitosis even with only a random distribution of the cytoplasmic contents. However as the number of such symbionts kept increasing, pushed on by the evolutionary pressure, the nucleus would have had to exert some control so the small genomes would not overwhelm everything else. It might have been possible but very difficult to evolve an apparatus to separate the organelles equally during mitotic cell divisions but it works nicely enough to have only a loose control of that and have the cells regulate the number of the organelles individually in the periods between divisions.

Of course the organelles need not have originated outside the early cells. They may have resulted from some separate packaging of genes that all originated in the host cell. In that case we would take the large number of organelles (and therefore their genomes) as a reflection of the cell's need for a high rate of synthesis of those essential proteins and their functions.

In the nucleus the control of the behavior of chromosomes and genes is strict but it is relaxed for the organelle genomes. The looser control of organelle regulation translates to the fact that more is left to chance in the organelles, possibly because there are many copies of them and they can multiply to meet the needs of the cells without the cell having to divide.

The evidence from studies in several species suggests that the organelle genomes are multiplied randomly which means that the numbers of each allelic gene type on those DNA molecules varies unpredictably and changes regularly as long as the organism is growing so that there are mitotic cell divisions occurring. The studies also suggest that some of the organelle genomes are destroyed by various mechanisms between cell divisions and again this seems somewhat random. The existing loose control thus leaves open the possibility of genetic drift in which an organelle may become genetically fixed in one condition and lose its adaptability due to chance events. In these cases that seems to be an acceptable price since things work well enough for the vast majority of individuals.

An advantage of the stringent controls in a one or two copy system like the nuclear genes is that the cells can show a high degree of heterozygosity and enjoy to the fullest the advantages of the gene-mixing that result from sexuality. Organelle genes cannot do that but considering their limited but vital functions a conservative approach is arguably safest and therefore best with them. The amazing part is that the two systems work harmoniously in the same cell.

In some plants both parents contribute mitochondrial and even chloroplast genomes to the zygotes but *selective silencing*, destructive processes targeted precisely at those from the male parent, removes them. In many animal species, including humans, the sperm cell contributes few if any mitochondria to the zygotes and even these few are likely to disappear. This leaves the cells with *maternal inheritance* in which all the functional genes for certain traits are received from the mother by way of the cytoplasm of the egg.

This one parent inheritance of organelle genomes may well reflect the advantages of asexual reproduction (of which it is a form) in maintaining adaptive combinations of alleles that might be broken up by recombination or scrambling, or by the spread of detrimental mutant genes within genomes that replicate more rapidly than the standard or wild type. Various researchers have indeed suggested that monogametic transmission and selective silencing may have both been selected for in evolution because they reduce the chance of organelle gene recombination.

The term *promiscuous* DNA entered the scientific dictionary in the early 1980s to describe the newly recognized fact that DNA sequences can and apparently have transferred between mitochondrion, chloroplast, and nucleus over time. Segments of the DNA sequences found in the chloroplast are found in the mitochondrion, and those of both chloroplast and mitochondrion are found in the nucleus. These organelles now both depend on huge imports of nuclear-coded proteins for their metabolic functions. It is assumed that they lost their independence over time by losing genes to the nucleus so finding the same sequences in the organelles and the nucleus is not a surprise but is in fact confirmation of the endosymbiont hypothesis. Finding them in both mitochondrion and chloroplast was a surprise since those had always been assumed to be independent of each other even though they have parallels in their chemical structures.

We might assume that initially the mitochondria could easily transfer genes to the nucleus but once the organelle's genetic code shifted from the universal one that would have become unlikely to succeed. This would have stranded some genes in the mitochondria in an evolutionary dead-end. When we examine the mitochondria genes of present day organism we find (as expected) no recognizable pattern to which of the genes were retained. It seems to have been a matter of chance exactly when the isolation was imposed on different ancestral groups. In some cases copies of transferred genes are found in the nucleus as well as in the mitochondria but those in the organelle are no longer used by the cell. Some types of flowering plants show the lowest rate of transfer of genes to the nucleus which results in them having larger mitochondrial genomes than other cell types.

How do the transfers occur? No one is certain but two suggestions are that either a transposable element or "jumping gene" is involved in each case or that the organelles sometimes physically fuse together within a cell. There is no reason to think there has to be a single mechanism for all the cases.

Much important study of mitochondrial genetics has been done in yeast cells that have the advantage of being able to survive by anaerobic fermentation if a mutation inactivates some function of the powerhouse. Such mutant yeast cells grow more slowly (one group are officially called pokey mutants) but they do not die without working mitochondria. Once researchers knew what to look for they began to recognize non-lethal, mutant forms in the mitochondria of other species, including ourselves.

Because, of its strict maternal inheritance in humans, mutations in mitochondrial DNA play an important role and have a disproportionate impact on hereditary disease and evolution. Such mutations would be expected to decrease the efficiency of the cells' energy release processes which would affect everything else but often without producing specific symptoms. In addition there are some genes that occur in both nuclear and mitochondrial DNA. Mutations in one or the other of these groups can produce disease with similar symptoms that may or may not show a Mendelian or nuclear inheritance pattern which just further confuses the diagnosis and delays the development of therapies.

Chapter 11

These are Rose's Chloroplasts

To some these are the green balls they saw in a leaf under the microscope at school. To others they are the source of the stuff called chlorophyll which they have heard of and think is supposed to be important but don't really know much about although they can remember that it was once touted as a breath purifier. To those in the know -- and that will now include you -- these are one of Nature's most wonderful inventions. These are Rose's chloroplasts, her photosynthetic machinery.

Chloroplasts or "green formed parts" are among the most conspicuous parts of the living world although they are seldom seen individually. They are also among the most important biological inventions of all times because they are the parts that allow the green plants to achieve three related and absolutely essential tasks in the one complex chemical process we call photosynthesis. First they trap solar energy in chemical bonds for later use. Second, in doing that they convert carbon dioxide gas into sugar molecules that are a basic food, which is to say energy and cell building substance. These sugars can then be chemically rearranged to form the other essential macromolecule types that are essential to and characterize life. And third, as a by-product of the food production they generate oxygen gas which is necessary for most living things to be able to use that food by releasing the energy from its molecular bonds. So this one process forms virtually all of the food for all of the living things of the entire world and maintains the high level of oxygen in the air that we need to survive. And it is a process that occurs only in the green plants and a few bacteria species. And in the plant cell it occurs only within these specialized structures.

The existence of chloroplasts has been known since the earliest days of microscopy in the 1700s and their function has been appreciated since the middle 1800s. The first detailed description of their structure was published by Meyer in 1880s.

Chloroplasts are meaningful only in an organized entity like a cell since they carry out a process needed for more than themselves and do so on a scale big enough to supply the needs of a larger unit like a whole cell. They are precisely organized, membrane-enclosed bodies within the mass of the plant cell. When the cell is viewed with a light microscope at 400 magnifications they appear as distinct green bubbles scattered around the cell without much conspicuous internal structure. When they are viewed with a transmission electron microscope at from 20,000 to 100,000 magnifications they are seen to be complex structures with large numbers of precisely arranged membrane sacs that have the green pigment materials embedded in the membranes.

These organelles are readily observed because they contain several pigment materials that are essential to their special activity and their color draws attention to them. They get their name from their color, which is the result of chlorophyll molecules that are the most abundant pigment molecules within them. It is the chlorophyll molecules that actually capture the units of light energy and transfer it to the molecules that are assembling the glucose precursors.

It is because there are several dozen chloroplasts in each typical photosynthetic plant cell -- and therefore 50,000 or more in every square millimeter of surface area --- that leaves and some stems look green. They actually define the photosynthetic plants as *green* plants. The microscopic view of a leaf is a surprise to many because they expect the entire call to be uniform green color but instead they find the green pigments are contained in many small, discrete, football-shaped bodies embedded in a more continuous mass of largely colorless cytoplasm.

The presence of chloroplasts is the major dividing trait between producers and consumers in the eucaryotic world of life. Photosynthesis or "putting together with light energy" results in an estimated 150 billion tons of sugar being formed by all the photosynthetic plants and bacteria on earth each year. This is the necessary energy input from outside to prevent the running down of all living systems that the Second Law of Thermodynamics predicts would otherwise be inevitable.

Only about 0.2% of the solar light reaching the surface of the planet is trapped in metabolically useful form. There are researchers who hope to improve the photosynthetic efficiency of major crop species by genetic engineering. We know which specific steps in the chemistry are limiting ones so if we can find more efficient forms of those proteins and transfer the genes for them into other species we might get them to produce more carbohydrate per acre per season.

Individual cells or organisms can and do get by with only energy release capacity and a fuel molecule supply but the overall system requires both those that can store energy and those that can release it. As a well balanced, sealed terrarium demonstrates, the photosynthetic plants do both and can get by quite nicely with only some microbial recyclers, no other consumers (and that means animals) are necessary.

Each chloroplast is microscopically small but they are often among the larger structures within a plant cell although their number, size, and shape varies from species to species. There is evidence that chloroplasts can change their shape or otherwise reorient themselves to light using proteins like actin that many animal cells use to move the cell or its parts. In the flowering plants like Rose they are usually oval and perhaps one-fourth the size of the nucleus.

Chemically, their dry weight is made up of about 55 percent proteins, 35 percent lipids, 8 percent chlorophyll molecules, one percent other pigments and some other molecules. Both chloroplasts and mitochondria contain DNA coding some of their molecules. This organelle DNA is structurally the same as the nuclear form but it is more loosely regulated and shows a few patterns the nuclear form does not.

Each of the dozens of them that are formed within and work within some but not all of the plant's cells is a complete working sugar factory by itself. Each contains many complete photosynthetic units that perform all the complex chemical steps to combine atoms from carbon dioxide (CO_2) and water (H_2O) into the more complex structure of the six-carbon simple sugar glucose ($C_6H_{12}O_6$) using light energy to form the necessary chemical bonds -- and in the process storing that energy for a later time when the chemical breakdown of the glucose sugar into carbon dioxide and water, whether, in cellular respiration or an open fire, will release that same amount of energy. Then Rose -- or, perish the thought -- some animal, that has fed on parts of her tissue and digested it, or ultimately the microbes that will get at whatever is left over when the plant or the animal is done, can use that energy to run their many metabolic chemical reactions that need it so they can stay alive.

Chloroplasts are one group of the plastids or "formed bodies" that are characteristic components of plant cells, but not found in animals. All plastids have a double layer of outer membrane wrapper and often a system of internal membranes that are surrounded by a uniform *stroma* (from the Greek for "something spread out") or ground substance. Three forms of plastids are regularly seen in plant cells, each type named for its color. The chloroplasts contain large amounts of the green chlorophylls and smaller amounts of carotenoid pigments. At times other pigments may be abundant enough in the cells to mask the presence of the chlorophyll but it is still there.

Chromoplasts ("colored formed bodies") contain mostly the lipid soluble red, yellow, and orange carotenoid pigments that they synthesize and retain and that are responsible for many flower petal and fruit colors. They may start as chloroplasts and convert as the chlorophyll and the internal membranes disappear and the carotenoids accumulate as happens in some ripening fruit like Rose's hips.

Leucoplasts ("white formed bodies") contain no pigment molecules but synthesize and store starch and other materials like oils and proteins. Almost 100% of the iron stored in plants is here attached to phytoferritin protein molecules. You see them in large numbers in a potato where they seem to have a white color when in groups. A plastid is a plastid, however, and when conditions require it they can change from one form to another. Leucoplasts sometimes become chloroplasts when exposed to light, and chloroplasts in the skin of a tomato will change into chromoplasts as the fruit ripens.

Membranes have a similar function anywhere that they occur in cells -- to regulate what gets in or out of some space. This is what happens within the structure of a chloroplast also. It contains large numbers of flattened membrane sacs called thylakoids (from the Greek for "sac like"), each formed with a double layer of membrane. For efficient packing the sacs are arranged in stacks, each stack called a granum (plural = grana), because that does not significantly reduce the efficiency of the processes going on inside the sacs. There are typically 40 to 60 grana in each chloroplast, all of them interconnected by inter-grana or stroma-thylakoids into a continuous membrane system that extends throughout the entire chloroplast.

In all cells, Rose's and your own, most of the chemical machinery that regulates and directs the many thousands of specific chemical reactions that must occur every second to maintain the special internal environment that we describe as alive are members of the group of protein molecule types, the many types that function as biological catalysts and are called enzymes. Each kind of enzyme produces one predictable effect when presented with the specific reagent molecule types for which it is designed and to which it must literally fit both to verify their identity and to bring about the reaction between them.

In cells complex tasks like the conversion of CO_2 and H_2O into sugar are performed in a series of small steps, each controlled by the appropriate enzyme, in something like assembly line fashion. To make this efficient the enzymes are fixed or attached to a membrane. The molecules being built up in a synthesis or broken down in a process like cellular respiration move easily from one enzyme to the next in the required sequence. That means that the enzymes must not only be fixed to a membrane but also must be the right distance apart and in the right order for the process to go as fast as practical. At each step in the process a valid type of molecule is formed and it is the type that will fit to the next enzyme so the next addition or alteration can occur. The membrane sacs of the chloroplast hold the many sets of the enzymes, the photosynthetic pigments, and the other pieces of molecular machinery in place.

The basic structural units of the light-requiring photosynthetic reactions are the granular appearing bodies that line the inside of the thylakoids. These are the ultimate energy trapping units, each containing 200 to 300 molecules of chlorophyll plus all the associated light gathering apparatus.

New chloroplasts can develop from *Proplastids* when for instance the tissue is initially exposed to light after being without it for a while. These small, poorly differentiated structures are probably always present in the cells although they are not usually obvious. They start as simple double membrane bubbles then the inner membrane folds into the flattened sacs that become fully developed grana and stroma thylakoids. At maturity there is no longer a physical connection between the inner membrane of the surrounding unit and the thylakoid system. A system of closed membrane units with distinct inside and outside is critical to the chemical processes of photosynthesis. There is no cholesterol in the thylakoid membrane and only about 25% of its lipid is phospholipid, most of the rest is glycolipid types not found anywhere else in cells.

New chloroplasts can also form by the division or fission of preexisting mature plastids whether the cell as a whole is dividing by mitosis or not. This division most resembles the process of binary fission in bacteria. This independence is one of the arguments for the Endosymbiont Hypothesis which proposes that these and some other organelle types started as free living procaryotic cell types. In this multiplication process the organelles replicate their DNA and may also switch equivalent genes between the DNA strands.

Once in a zygote the organelle DNA (but not usually the nuclear DNA) continues to switch pieces between strands during the mitotic divisions of the cells so after twenty or so generations of cells have formed in the embryo the nuclear DNA pattern is the same in each cell but there may be significant chances in the distribution of the organelle DNA in them.

This latter is best understood from an example. In some geraniums (which are botanically hybrids called *Pelargonium* X *hortorum)* the leaf cells contain chloroplast genes that produce either normal green chloroplasts or white ones. If a plant with all green chloroplast genes and one with green and white genes are interbred the resulting zygotes are of three types in variable proportions. Some are all green, some are a mix of green and white, and some have only genes for white chloroplasts. These latter die as seedlings because they cannot photosynthesize, which also explains why they can never be used as parents in this type of breeding experiment. As they grow into embryos and mature plants the green zygotes will remain all green (except for an occasional new mutation) but the green-white mixed individuals will gradually develop more green or more white cells (as long as the plant retains enough functional chloroplasts to survive).

Each cell in the mature variegated plant is homozygous for the cytoplasmic or organelle genes. A variegated leaf has some green cells and some white ones, each with only that type of gene for the trait even though the zygotes of these biparental individuals contained both the green and the white genes. What happened? Each cycle of mitotic division there was a possibility of vegetative segregation in which the green and the white genes may switch places between the homologous strands of DNA. This same thing can happen between nuclear genes but only during a cell division by meiosis. If there is no segregation, the green and white genes become two copies each and one of each goes into each daughter cell which therefore remains like the parent cell for this trait. There is the possibility though that after the copies have formed both copies of the green gene can go into one cell while both white genes go into the other cell -- so both daughter cells are now homozygous for the trait. The shift is always toward more and eventually all homozygous cells because once the cell has only one form of the gene rearrangements can and do occur as often as before but the result is always the same since the other gene form is no longer present in the cell. And this is a process going on in each cell separately. This is why the variegation pattern may change somewhat as the leaf matures but is fixed once the leaf is full size.

Choloroplasts often contain temporary oil storage units in the form of droplets or starch grains that form during active photosynthesis but are likely to disappear after some time in the dark as sugars and other nutrient molecules are either used by the cell to maintain its own metabolism or transported elsewhere in the plant. They also contain small ribosomes and some DNA.

Today we understand virtually all of the chemistry of photosynthesis at the molecular level and all the textbooks casually give the details that hundreds of researchers spent long years working out. We will not go through those details here, only note the overall reaction that has some important general implications. Carbon dioxide plus water, with an input of energy and in the presence of chlorophyll, yields glucose sugar plus oxygen gas.

The raw materials then are carbon dioxide and water. This leads us to suspect that, up to a point, the increase in the amount of $CO2$ in the air as a result of the large scale burning of fossil fuels (that trapped the energy eons ago by photosynthesis) in the last century and a half has been minimized by a combination of increased photosynthetic rates and absorption into the oceans where it eventually forms calcium carbonate and other compounds that settle into long term storage in shells and sediments that eventually become limestone. The need for a supply of water makes the plant's vascular system essential. Neither of these materials is usually a limiting factor but either can be.

In 1905 English plant physiologist F.F. Blackman accurately proposed that photosynthesis occurs in two stages and only the first requires light energy. We now call those that will not occur without light and which increase in rate as the light intensity increases the *light reactions*, or more properly the light-requiring reactions. Now that we understand much of the chemistry involved we know that in this stage light energy is used to generate ATPs from ADPs.

The *dark reactions* are more properly the light-independent reactions because they can occur in the dark but do not require it. These increase in rate if the temperature increases but not if the light intensity does. In this phase the products of the first stage are used to convert carbon dioxide into simple sugars which are energy in a storable, easily transportable form that also has a carbon skeleton so it can be used to form other organic molecule types. These reactions occur in the stroma which also contains the organelle's own DNA, RNAs. and ribosomes.

There are two phases to the chemistry of food-making and separate areas of the chloroplasts where each occurs. The light energy is absorbed in the pigments within the thylakoid membranes but the sugars are assembled in the matrix between the membranes.

To be used, light energy must be absorbed into molecules and then transferred into molecular bonds. The molecule types that absorb light are called pigments and each absorbs some but not all energy levels or wavelengths of light. The wavelengths not absorbed are either reflected or transmitted and those are the ones we use to describe the color of the object. The chlorophyll molecules absorb blue and red wave lengths and reflect green.

When a pigment absorbs light energy some electrons within it are boosted to a higher energy level. Think of a ball that you can swing on a string. You start off easy and it goes in a small circle down almost at the level it was before you moved it. The harder you twirl it though (the more energy you give the ball) the wider the cone of air it goes around and the closer to the plane of your hand it rises. Electrons can change energy levels without leaving an atom is an analogous way. Such energy may be reradiated immediately as light energy at a higher wavelength (=fluorescence), reradiated later as light energy (=phosphorescence), dissipated as heat, or it may be captured in a chemical bond as happens in photosynthesis.

Between them the chlorophylls and the carotenoids can absorb much of the visible spectrum. The several pigment molecule types work as a unit, collecting photons of energy and passing them from molecule to molecule to a *chlorophyll a* molecule at the reaction center of the individual photosynthetic unit. This reaction center is a place into which energy can flow more or less continuously during photosynthesis both because it is the lowest energy molecule of the group and energy, like water, seeks the lowest level and because it is rapidly transferring energy to other parts of the apparatus so it is essentially emptying as fast as it fills, thus it is referred to as an energy *sink*.

There are two separate light-absorbing photosystems (PS), one that operates at the 700nm wavelength, the other at 680 nm. Each contains a group of pigment molecule types and some of the components act as channels through the thylakoid membrane. The two systems are interconnected in that they work in series.

Energy trapped in the 680nm system (called PSII because it was discovered after the other) is transferred in the form of high-energy electrons to the 700nm or PSI system.

In simplest form the light energy allows the pigments in the PSII to raise the energy level of electrons and strip them from water molecules. This leaves the oxygen atoms to combine as oxygen gas and escape into the air. PSII transfers the electrons to PSI and from there they enter an electron transport chain where in a series of reactions they release the energy which is used to form ATPs while the hydrogen ions or protons from the water are bonded to the coenzyme NADP to form $NADH^+$ which will transport them to the matrix also to become the hydrogens of the sugar- molecules.

Using a heavy oxygen ^{18}O isotope researchers have been able to trace water through the process and show that the water that is a raw material of the process is the source of the oxygen gas that comes out as a by-product, not the oxygens from the other raw material, carbon dioxide. This makes it the exact complement of cell respiration which we saw in the last chapter requires oxygen in order to form water. Since chloroplasts release oxygen and mitochondria require it, it seems likely that mitochondria evolved after and perhaps even from chloroplasts.

The primary function of chloroplasts is photosynthesis. Except for some bacteria types, cells without chloroplasts cannot carry out photosynthesis but isolated chloroplasts can perform the chemistry in a test tube. Chloroplasts also perform some other important functions. In the stroma they convert some nitrogen compounds to ammonia, and sulfate ions to molecules of the sulfur-containing amino acid cysteine. They synthesize long chain fatty acids that will be used to make lipid energy storage molecules while simultaneously inactivating hydrogen peroxide unavoidably formed in some of the reactions by a process that uses ascorbic acid or vitamin C. They also synthesize those unique glycolipids for the thylakoid membranes.

"Photosynthetic animals" are always found to have symbiotic algae living within their tissues, none have been found with chloroplast of their own making.

Chapter 12

THESE ARE ROSE'S OTHER CELLULAR "BUBBLES"

There are several other named organelles found in Rose's and most cells although at least one of them is typical of plant but not of animal cells. Some of these were literally unknown before we saw the insides of cells with the electron microscope and the others were suspected to exist but their nature and especially their functions were not known. What ties them together is that they are all membrane-enclosed, fluid-filled bubbles or sacs. What differentiates them is the specific materials they contain. Although we cannot trace everything yet we feel certain from a variety of bits and pieces of experimental evidence that these different structures interact with one another in various ways to achieve the ends of the cell.

A feature of most mature plant cells that is almost never seen in normal animal cells is the presence of a large water filled bubble or *vacuole* that occupies fifty percent or more of the volume of the cell. The single bilayer membrane that encloses it is called the *tonoplast*, a good example of the value of scientific terminology since the single word replaces the first seven of this sentence. The tonoplast is closely associated with the ER and in some species is clearly seen to be continuous with that membrane system in photomicrographs. It has different permeabilities than the plasma membrane which means it lets in and out some molecule types that cannot as readily get in or out of the cell as a whole.

The origin of the vacuoles is not clear. They are often detectable as small separate membrane-enclosed units in the young cell that gradually combine in the way that oil droplets floating on a liquid do and form a single large unit but it is not clear whether they are formed from scratch or from some small inherited particles the way chloroplasts are.

This vacuole acts as a convenient storage area for various water-soluble materials that can be quickly put into storage or removed as needed so they are not lost from the cell. Water soluble pigments like the anthocyanins accumulate in there rather than being dispersed through the whole cytoplasm. Most of the color of rose petals is concentrated in the vacuole liquid.

Metabolic waste products may also be stored in the vacuole since there is not an obvious way for the deeper located plant cells to get rid of such materials without blood and kidneys. The salt concentration inside can become high enough for crystals to form in there. In some cases the vacuole fluid is so acidic it would damage the general cytoplasm if the tonoplast were to rupture, an indication of the difference a membrane can make. The waste products and other stored material may be distasteful or even poisonous to animals that attempt to eat the plant, a benefit derived from an unavoidable condition.

The bubble also has the useful effect of pressing the cytoplasm against the surrounding cell wall so that the unit is firm and strong in the way that a properly inflated auto tire depends on the air inside to hold the rubber and other materials in a firm weight supporting condition.

Calcium ion (Ca^{+2}) is important for the regulation of many cellular processes within the cytoplasm of plant cells as well as in various operations in which some stimulus is transmitted. In animal cells the Ca^{+2} moves through selective channels in the plasma membrane and the enclosing membranes of the organelles (mostly the ER) to meet the needs with calcium ion pumps and mechanisms that exchange sodium ions for calcium ions to balance things. In plants the Ca^{+2} regulates photosynthesis, phototropism and gravitropism, and ion fluxes in the vacuoles and plasma membrane. Calcium ions can be sequestered or stored in the ER or in the vacuole to reduce the level in the cytoplasm without losing it. There are voltage dependent calcium channels in plant vacuoles that allow this regulation.

As various organelles age and degrade they are moved across the tonoplast and digested within the central vacuole and many of the component small molecules are recycled.

Dictyosomes were first reported by the Italian cytologist Camillio Golgi in 1898 in sections of neurons treated with an osmium tetroxide stain that was in later years replaced by one using silver salts. For years some argued that these were not cell structures but only artifacts produced by the staining process. The electron microscope pictures resolved the matter.

The terminology is still in flux and many authors use the terms interchangeably but some argue for the distinction that the dozens to hundreds of small groups of sacs that are typical of plant cells are dictyosomes but the single large unit formed by the aggregation of many sac groups seen in many animal cell types is to be called the Golgi Apparatus or Golgi Body.

Seen in virtually all eucaryotic cells these organelles are usually seen in the cut section views with the electron microscope as a stack of three to seven thin, flattened but somewhat curved membrane sacs. When seen head-on the edges of the roundish sacs have a lacy appearance which we now know results from small bits pulling off to form small membrane-enclosed vesicles that travel through the cytoplasm to become parts of the plasma membrane or that of the various organelles, usually transporting some newly synthesized materials inside them and delivering those in the process.

In many photomicrographs the sacs seem to be unconnected but techniques that provide a 3-D view suggest they are all connected into one continuous structure by thin tubes around the edges.

Each has a definite polarity with the membrane thickness and the cholesterol content changing from its concave to its convex face. Some enzymes are concentrated on one face or the other and there may be compositional and functional differences between the edges and the center of the disks.

The dictyosomes maintain, expand, and recycle many of the lipids and some of the proteins of the cell membranes. They also assemble glycolipids and glycoproteins, chemically process other molecule types, play a role in the formation of some other organelles like lysosomes in animal cells, and regulate the transport of various materials around the cell within vesicles.

During the processing of the glycoproteins the "immature" molecules move from enzymes in one sac to those in adjacent sacs while packaged within vesicles. These small units arrive from the ER at the forming face of the dictyosome sac and the enclosed materials pass from sac to sac and emerge as vesicles again from the *maturing face*. They then move off as finished products packaged for delivery. An extensive variety of materials are moved all around the cell inside vesicles. For instance the dictyosome helps sort various newly formed proteins and direct them to the appropriate organelle, membrane, or other cell region where they will function or be released as exports. The major unknown is how the dictyosome knows what needs to go where and how it codes the vesicles so they get to the right addresses. We have some general ideas but not many of the details yet.

Part of the answer to how traffic control of molecules occurs is tied into the fact that dictyosomes contain glycosyl transferases, enzymes that catalyze the polymerization of sugars into polysaccharides, especially the hemicelluloses, pectins, and other polysaccharides that assemble outside the cell to form the cell wall. They also attach the sugars to glycolipids and glycoproteins. The multiple-sugar or oligosaccharide side chains of glycoproteins and glycolipids are probably critical to the sorting and shipping processes that get the correct molecule types to each organelle or area and assure that the molecules face the right way, either into an enclosed space or on the outside of the plasma membrane or the organelle.

The formation of glycoproteins occurs in stages. First the peptide chain is formed then the sugar units are bonded on. This second stage can occur while sections of the peptide chain are still being assembled by the ribosomes one amino acid at a time or it may not happen until the peptide chain has been folded into its mature, functional 3-D shape. The ER and the dictyosome play roles in this overall operation with the first steps occurring as the protein is assembled and immediately enters the lumen of the ER to fold into shape and the later processing steps taking place after the molecules are moved to the dictyosome within a vesicle.

Within the dictyosome the membrane of a vesicle can be modified so that its composition matches that of the plasma membrane or that of whatever organelle it will deliver materials to because to achieve that end the vesicle must insert its lipid covering into the target membrane without disrupting the continuity of that layer. In some cases the vesicle lipid layer is made unique so it cannot fuse with any membrane in the cell.

In *Drosophyllum lusitanicum*, an insect-eating plant closely related to the sundews, about 100 dictyosome vesicles must deliver materials every minute to produce the visible drops of enzyme-filled fluid that appear on the leaf glands and act both as a sticky trap to catch the insects and an external stomach to digest them. Such secretary cells would double their plasma membrane every twenty seconds if the vesicle membrane were not being rapidly recycled back to the ER and the dictyosomes. The mucilage-secreting cells of root caps have about 800 dictyosomes each that together produce enough vesicle membrane to double the size of the plasma membrane every 20 to 40 minutes if it were not being recycled.

Many of the vesicles leaving the dictyosome contain concentrated complexes of several different products --- protein, carbohydrates, or combinations of one or both of those with lipids. This makes for efficient transport since there is a maximum of payload with a minimum of bulk.

Peroxisomes ("peroxide containing bodies") were first identified by Christian deDuve in the 1960s. These are unit membrane enclosed organelles characterized by the presence of any of a family of related molecule types that generate hydrogen peroxide (H_2O_2) during specific chemical reactions and contain catalase enzymes that promptly convert the peroxide into water and oxygen gas. Several essential reactions inevitably generate highly reactive and therefore dangerous peroxide as a by-product and it is also needed as a reagent for certain digestive operations essential to the cells. By conducting these reactions within a protective space and in close proximity to the catalase enzymes the rest of the cell is protected without having to sacrifice the processes that involve these dangerous steps.

The peroxisomes are involved in both the synthesis and the degradation of various lipids. Especially noteworthy is that they contain a beta-oxidation enzyme pathway that lets them degrade very long chain fatty acids. This is a variation on the enzyme pathway in mitochondria that allows fatty acids to be oxidized or "burned" in addition to or in place of glucose to supply the cell's metabolic energy. The system in the mitochondria can handle fatty acid chains fewer than six carbons long but the one in the peroxisomes can only process longer chains than that. These organelles cooperate in photorespiration in photosynthetic tissues. This is a poorly understood but no doubt important process (since it is so widespread and involves so many choreographed chemical steps) that seems to actually waste the effort put into photosynthesis.

In plants a special type of peroxisome called a *glyoxysome* can convert fatty acids into the precursor molecule types that can be readily processed into glucose molecules, a process that animal cells cannot accomplish. This is used mainly in the seeds where lipid stored in the endosperm is made into glucose for the use of the embryo during germination. These cells have normal peroxisomes in addition.

The peroxisomes have variable shape but it takes chemical analysis of the contents to positively identify them. They are usually roughly spherical, enclosed by a single bilayer membrane, and contain no DNA. The bubbles are filled with a slightly acidic fluid matrix that has many of the important proteins that carry out its functions dissolved in it. All the proteins including those embedded in the organelle's membrane are synthesized in the cytoplasm and then moved into the peroxisomes as mature functional proteins, not as some kind of inactive precursors.

Peroxisomes are present in all eucaryotic cells and a human deficiency disease called Zellweger syndrome indicates that eucaryotic organisms cannot long survive without them. Their number varies from one or two per cell in yeasts to thousands in an egg cell. Sometimes they are seen in close groups and these may be interconnected. As with the detoxification reactions at smooth ER, some of the enzymes in the peroxisomes are inducible, being rapidly produced when needed but not present all the time. New organelles seem to be produced as the result of the growth and then division of existing ones.

Lysosomes are smaller vacuoles in a variety of plant cells that enclose acid hydrolases and other digestive enzymes, which is the defining feature of this organelle. These structures were recognized and studied in animal cells not long after the electron microscope gave us some idea that such membrane-enclosed bubbles exist in cells. They were identified as being used for digestion of foreign materials within certain kinds of cells and for the digestion of worn out components of the cell itself. They are also used when cells need to remove themselves from the scene, effectively committing suicide by dissolving themselves from the inside as happens at various stages in many animal embryos. In plants they dissolve all the cell contents and leave the intact cell wall as happens to produce the water-conducting xylem tubes. They are also used to selectively remove no longer functional or needed structures within the cell.

The hydrolases that are used to define which membrane enclosed bubbles are lysosomes are a class of enzymes that split a molecule of water in the process of splitting some macromolecule according to the general formula $A1-A_2 + H_2O \rightarrow A1-H + A_2-OH$. Their contents can totally digest cells because they include hydrolases for all of the major macromolecule groups -- proteins, carbohydrates, lipids, and nucleic acids.

There is evidence that the early stages of the formation of the central vacuole involves areas of cytoplasm being surrounded by new membrane and the contents subsequently removed by *autophagy* or "self eating" to form the small vacuoles that will eventually fuse to become the large central one. The same kind of autophagy occurs as leaves and flowers wither before being shed, allowing usable organic and inorganic chemicals to be recovered for reuse before those parts are disconnected and the plant would need to depend on their decomposition in the soil by microbes to recycle anything and that only the minerals.

Autophagy may be a way for cells to survive periods of starvation, stress, or metabolic emergency by digesting parts of their cytoplasm to provide metabolites for the rest so the whole unit does not die.

CHAPTER 13

THESE ARE ROSE'S TISSUES

Tissues are groups of similar cells organized into a structural and functional unit in which they cooperate to perform some overall functions that the cells cannot achieve effectively as single units. The tissues are the basic multicellular components of plant and animal bodies, each consisting of several to many individual cells, and cells are the fundamental working units of any living thing. Probably the cells adjust themselves into their respective tissues more easily that they would in some free form state and there is clear evidence that signals between adjacent cells are important in deciding their specialties. Some tissues, like individual muscles, need to work as a cooperative unit to produce the desired effect. In most though the effect seems to be simply the accumulation of the work of the individual cells, and their concentration for better control and distribution seems to be the main advantage of the grouping.

It is often easier for us to understand and describe the structure and function of multicellular organisms by considering the relatively few kinds of tissues rather than the many cells with a variety of large and small differences. In the same way that when we are only concerned with general features and a description of the overall functions, not the details of how they happen, we think of houses as being composed of walls and floors rather than of bricks and sticks, so also we tend to focus on the larger structural units of a plant's anatomy. Cells are bricks, tissues are pre-formed wall units that can be thought of as being fitted into place to do a job (although they are actually assembled there cell by cell). A tissue may also include some noncellular material secreted by the cell as part of its structure like the pectin associated with plant cell walls and the stiff jelly-like matrix substances of bone, cartilage, and other connective tissues in animals like ourselves.

In the vascular plants like Rose the main tissue types are organized into the embryonic or nonpermanent tissues, called the meristems, and three permanent tissue systems that extend throughout the plant body. The *ground tissue system* makes up most of the photosynthetic and the "filler" material of most plant organs, including the various secretary structures like idioblasts and laticifers. The *vascular tissue system* forms the water and nutrient transport system of tubes throughout the plant body and also provides much of its strength. The dermal *tissue* system forms the outer protective covering of all the other parts. The fact that these same permanent tissue types run continuously through leaf, stem and root emphasizes the continuity of the plant body and the similarity of its component parts. In the same way, the less specialized connective tissue types in the human body are part of each and every other organ.

Tissues may be defined either by the type of cells that make them up or by their position without regard to what kind of cells are in them. The three types of ground tissue are defined largely on the basis of the characteristics of the cells themselves. The cortex and pericycle, on the other hand, are defined mainly by their position in the plant organ. Such tissues as epidermis, xylem, phloem and meristem have both a characteristic position and a characteristic structure.

A tissue is classified as simple if it is made up of only one microscopically distinct type of cell and *complex* if composed of two or more types. This distinction is important when examining microscopic views of the tissues because it alerts you to whether there will be one or several sizes and shapes of cells that should be considered part of the functional unit. The ground tissues are simple, vascular and dermal tissues are complex.

The three types of ground tissues are parenchyma, collenchyma, and sclerenchyma. They are the most structurally uniform since each is composed of a single kind of cell. These are the tissues that do most of the photosynthesizing, nutrient processing and storage, and secretion throughout the plant so they are the material which the other tissues surround and support in one sense or another.

Parenchyma gets its name from the Greek *para* "by the side of" and *enchein*, meaning "to pour in". The *-enchyma* reflects the long held view that these ground tissue cells were literally poured in to fill the spaces between the other, more specialized, tissues. Now we realize they remain scattered among the other cell types as much to be available to form replacement or additional specialized types if needed as just to fill up space.

Parenchyma tissue is the primary tissue type from which all the others will develop during the growth and development of the plant. Parenchyma cells are the least specialized, most general-purpose cells in the plant. The shape of a cell is dictated in part by the special job it has to do. The parenchyma cell has the least specialized shape because it is adaptable and may be called upon to change into any of the more specialized tissue types. The shape of parenchyma cells is determined by the way they press up against the other cells around them. Generally they are of more or less equal length in all three dimensions, a shape called isodiametric. The engineer's tell us that the theoretically ideal shape for packing equal-sized soft spheres together in the smallest space so that they compress and shape one another with the minimum space left between them is a fourteen-sided polyhedron with eight five-sided and six square faces, a figure called an *orthic tetrakaidecahedron*. Closely packed parenchyma cells often end up with a shape close to this ideal. The major reason they do not actually match the ideal is that land plant cells almost always have some air spaces between individual cells to facilitate the exchange of oxygen and carbon dioxide with the outside air so that only some of their fourteen surfaces will be fully pressed against another cell.

The parenchyma cells usually have a thin cell wall composed mainly of cellulose and pectin materials and with no secondary thickening. When functioning these cells are alive and retain a nucleus so they are still capable of cell division. This is important because this tissue is then capable of undergoing major modifications in the number and specialization of its cells when that is required ---- for instance, to repair wounds or to replace parts eaten by animals. Some other kinds of cells are dead when they do their important work for the plant so they cannot repair themselves if they become damaged or blocked. For this reason there are usually a few parenchyma cells left among the other tissues to grow and differentiate and do the repairs when and if that becomes necessary. They may also have a role in keeping dead xylem tubes open so those can conduct water but this is not clear. We do know that as the older tissue changes from sapwood to heartwood the parenchyma die and the tubes start to clog up and become non-conducting although they still supply strength.

Parenchymous tissues often contain chloroplasts. In fact, most photosynthetic tissues are parenchyma. It is sometimes useful to call those parenchyma cells that contain chloroplasts *chlorenchyma* ("chlorophyll poured in"), not to be confused with collenchyma.

In the primary plant body, the part that develops directly from the terminal meristem, the parenchyma typically forms continuous masses of cells in the cortex of stems and roots, the pith of stems, the mesophyll of leaves, and the flesh of fruits. When you bite into an apple or a tomato, most of what you are munching on is parenchyma tissue. Most storage cells in plants are parenchyma.

The cortex (from the Latin for bark or rind) is a tissue layer that contributes strength and food storage everywhere and sometimes also photosynthesis in the shoot. It is positioned between the central vascular cylinder and the epidermis in various patterns depending on the species and the body part. Sometimes there is also a pericycle ("around the circle") layer between the endodermis and the vascular cylinder. Both of these are made up mostly of typical parenchyma cells and get their special names because of their position.

Some parenchyma cells have special finger-shaped growths on the inside of their cell walls. These increase the surface area of the cell membrane and probably allow the cells to function more efficiently in transferring dissolved materials rapidly from one adjacent cell to another. These cells are referred to as *transfer cells*. There is growing evidence that they are important in intensive short-distance transfer of materials between the vascular conducting system and other cells throughout the entire plant body.

The turgor (internal water pressure) of the parenchyma cells, that typically have large central vacuoles, is a major means of support for herbaceous plants that lack any extensive woody tissue.

Collenchyma tissue, composed of collenchyma cells, gets its name from the Greek *colla*, "glue" --- referring to their thick cell walls that are tightly attached to one another and have a glistening "just glued" appearance in fresh material. The cell walls are composed only of cellulose and pectin materials but they are much thicker than those of parenchyma and the thickening is usually unequally distributed. Especially where two or more of these cells touch one another they form extra thick corners of cellulose for reinforcement.

The principal function of collenchyma is support and mechanical. strengthening of non-woody tissues. It forms the first supporting tissue in young stems and leaves and is important in many mature ones as well. Because their cell walls do not contain lignins or other secondary strengthening materials these cells are still capable of growth and even division by mitosis. Under the influence of a special enzyme the thick cellulose walls offer relatively little resistance. to stretching during elongation of the plant part and because the cells are alive they can continue to make and deposit new cell wall material during this growth process. These cells also allow regeneration or replacement of lost parts and reinforcement of wounded areas, even in the herbaceous stems. The addition of lignins to the cell walls, which effectively makes them into wood, stops the growth process in that area because the cell walls can no longer be stretched and then reconstructed into larger shapes. A comparable situation occurs in ourselves. Our growth period ends when the ends of the long bones of our limbs become fully calcified after puberty because the bones can not get longer once the cartilage plates or epiphyses that separate sections of those bones and allow new material to add to their length are converted into bone tissue.

Collenchyma cells usually have a well developed central vacuole and often contain chloroplasts. These cells are typically longer than wide and form distinct strands or continuous cylinders beneath the epidermis in stems and petioles. They also border the veins in Dicot leaves, giving those additional strength. They are not as often found in roots. A good place to examine collenchyma is in a stalk of celery. The "strings" on the outer surface of the stalks (that are actually leaf petioles) are made almost entirely of collenchyma.

The other ground tissue is sclerenchyma, another support tissue. These cells derive their name from the Greek *skleros*, meaning "hard" which describes the thick, often lignified, secondary cell walls that are their main characteristic. Sclerenchyma cells are important strengthening and support components in plant parts. They may develop in any part of the plant at any stage of its life cycle. These cells are often dead at maturity when they are performing this support function.

Sclerenchyma is distinct from the two other common support and strengthening tissues in both structure and location. It differs from collenchyma because it contains lignin or other secondary cell wall materials and it only develops in plant parts after they have stopped elongating and growing. Sclerenchyma and xylem are both composed of thick-walled, lignified, dead cells but they differ on three points. Sclerenchyma is a simple tissue, it has an exclusively support function, and it may develop anywhere in the plant. Xylem is a complex tissue, it has water conduction as well as support functions, and it is limited to a few specific areas of the plant body.

There are two distinct types of sclerenchyma cells coming from different origins: fibers and sclereids. Fibers are long, thick-walled cells that commonly occur in bundles or strands. Each fiber typically forms from a new cell produced by mitosis from the meristem, As this cell grows it adds a lignified secondary cell wall and eventually dies, leaving a cell wall skeleton to strength the plant part. These fibers have considerable strength and they have important commercial uses. Paper, for instance, is composed mainly of a mixture of sclerenchyma fibers and xylem cells from wood. The component plant fibers are especially easy to see in paper toweling or pulpy tablet paper. Jute *(Corchorus* species) fibers used in twine and flax *(Linum* usitatissium) fibers that make linen are typical of those processed from Dicot stems. Manila hemp or *abaca* comes from the stems of *Musa textilis*, a Monocot and a close relative of the banana. Not all "fibers" derived from plants are sclerenchyma fibers though. Cotton *(Gossypium* spp.) fibers are epidermal hairs of the seeds, not sclerenchyma cells, and are composed almost entirely of cellulose.

Sclereids are relatively short cells that have thick, lignified secondary cell walls and a variable shape. Often they are branched and irregularly shaped. They may occur singly or in groups, scattered among other cell types. Either parenchyma or collenchyma may turn into sclerenchyma if they develop lignified secondary cell walls as they age. These cells are sometimes referred to as stone cells because they make up the seed coats of seeds, the shells of nuts, and the pits of the stone fruits like cherries and peaches. Such sclereids are what gives the flesh of pears its characteristic gritty texture.

Using the analogy that a plant is like a factory, the parenchyma cells are the machines for making sugar by photosynthesis and then other kinds of molecules from the sugar that the building is constructed to house. The collenchyma are the temporary beams and 2X4 studs that are put into place to allow the operation of the factory to continue while more permanent construction lags behind. The sclerenchyma are the braces and columns that will form the permanent structure for the long run. To continue the analogy, like a factory a plant has the supply pipes centrally located and support beams scattered throughout to hold up the roof. The production machinery is arranged around the supply pipes and between the roof supports without one function interfering with the other and the protective waterproof outer wall has windows (stomates) that can be opened to let in air but closed for security at night.

The second tissue system is the vascular tissues, the fluid conducting tubes that create the plant's circulation. This is the tissue system that distinguishes the higher or more modern plants, the ferns and the flowering plants, from the more ancient forms like algae and mosses. Tall land plants only became a possibility when the plant's developed a way to get water from the ground to the body parts a distance above it and to get some of the food materials being formed by photosynthesis in the above ground parts back to the roots and other essential structures to supply their nutrient needs since they have given up their own ability to make food to make this tall growth possible. Until some kind of a translocation system developed land plants simply could not grow more than a few inches tall. But growing taller would give the advantage of exposing greater surfaces to the sunlight and thus increase the amount of food that could be produced by photosynthesis. Until vascular plants developed there was only a low green slime over any part of the land. Once they appeared in the form of the ferns and their relatives, most of which are now long extinct, giant forests developed and changed the world in dramatic ways.

The fluid transport or vascular system consists of xylem and phloem, both complex tissues including several sizes or shapes of cells. They represent the conveyor belts and pipes delivering raw materials from the delivery ramp at the roots to the manufacturing machines above and then distributing the finished products to all the departments of the factory for use, storage or shipping.

As tissues reach maturity the middle lamella between the cell walls usually breaks down a bit at the edges and angles so that air spaces develop that gradually become more or less continuous throughout the mass of cells. These are critical to the survival of the deep located cells in a land plants because without a blood-type fluid to deliver or remove oxygen and carbon dioxide as the cells need them they would literally suffocate.

The dermal system contains the protective cork of the outer bark and the cork cambium that forms and usually becomes distinct from the more deeply located vascular cambium that makes new vascular tissue cells.

Secondary tissues are defined as those formed from a cambium rather than an apical meristem. They include cork and secondary xylem and phloem.

Together these allow the growth in diameter that is necessary so that an area of root or stem can accommodate the additional numbers of vascular tubes that will be needed to handle the increased volume of transport materials to and from the structures that form beyond that point over time. In most Monocots and some herbaceous Dicots the tissues of the procambium all mature so there is no lateral meristem and therefore no secondary tissues.

Meristem tissue is a group of cells that remain immature or undifferentiated so they are able to divide by mitosis without difficulty to produce new cells that can then mature into any and all of the types the plant needs. They are concentrated in a few specific parts and are classified by those positions as tip or apical, lateral or cambial, and intercalary. The latter, most notable in the internodes of grass stems, are inserted or intercalated between more or less differentiated tissues some distance from the apical meristem. Meristems are present to allow growth and repair.

CHAPTER 14

THIS IS ASEXUAL REPRODUCTION IN ROSE

Asexual reproduction has been around since Year One on the calendar of cellular living things on the planet – otherwise life would never have gotten beyond that point. Organized masses of molecules were curiosities but nothing more until they became self-replicating units. At that point the possibility of change entered the picture because the genetic system based on coded instructions stored as nucleic acid molecules was established and the one-in-a-million errors or alterations in that code would allow mutations and subsequently diversity as different cell lines became better adapted to different sets of environmental conditions. The physical reality is that local climatic conditions can change substantially and both quickly and unpredictably so a mechanism that produces a reasonable degree of genetic diversity as quickly as possible and maintains it in every generation would be an advantage. Thus when the diploid or pairs of genes for each trait condition developed there was evolutionary or survival advantage for those organisms that developed sexual reproduction which requires genetic mixing in each event. The advantage was great enough that many forms stuck in an asexual-reproduction-only pattern were undoubtedly outcompeted and squeezed into extinction by comparable types with greater genetic diversity within their populations.

However that did not mean that types with only asexual reproduction but no better adapted competitors, or those forms that retained some capacity for asexual reproduction along with a sexual process, all disappeared. Not by a long shot. Most of the vast numbers and numbers of kinds of microorganisms remain resolutely asexual and many plants have at least some capacity for it. There are instances of asexual multiplication among multicellular animals but the capacity is virtually unknown among the more highly evolved forms of invertebrates and I believe totally unknown among the vertebrates. Some of the higher animals can still regenerate severed parts – like a lizard growing a new tail – but the tail cannot grow a new lizard.

Asexual reproduction is simply growth with the hitch that it involves not just expansion of existing parts but the formation of all the other parts needed to make this into a full and independent individual. The case most are familiar with is the stem cutting that grows new roots to become a whole plant. In a few cases, African violets are a familiar example, a single leaf can give rise to a group of new plants. Leaves have the quirk that they give rise to one or more new young plants but they themselves are not part of any of those. Although the parent leaf may develop some roots during the process it does not regenerate a stem for itself. In a few cases, with dandelions being an annoying example, a section of root left in the ground when the top growth is pulled off may regrow the whole shoot.

It is precisely because most desirable crop and ornamental species and cultivars are highly heterozygous (have copies of different allelic forms of many of their genes) and therefore would produce sexual offspring with a wide variety of different combinations of traits, most or all of them less desirable than the combinations in the parents, that asexual propagation is important in agriculture. It is also often faster, cheaper, and more reliable since in some important species the seeds may hold everything up by remaining dormant for many months or even years despite everything we know how to do to active them. In many fruit tree species that have a long juvenile growth stage before they mature so they can flower, the asexual offspring of a mature plant are themselves genetically mature already so they will flower as soon as they are large enough, often years before their seed siblings.

It seems safe to assume that organisms reproduced asexually before they evolved the sexual capacity and it makes sense that types that could maintain both options would be better off than those with only one. A major impact of the plant growth pattern is that it provides this option of vegetative reproduction as an adjunct to seed production and generally without interfering with the sexual processes.

There are several advantages to asexual or vegetative propagation, starting with the fact that flowers are not required. As many plant people can tell you, finding and providing the conditions that will induce flowering in many species is a mighty challenge. Some types will go on for years without producing a bud while others of their species and of the same age growing someplace else are blooming their heads off.

There is a definite if somewhat short term logic to asexual reproduction. The plant that is multiplying is doing well enough now (despite the ravages of external forces like the storm that broke off some pieces or the animal that chewed some and dropped a few crumbs in the process) that its clone should prosper under the general climatic conditions of the area. In the short run a plant that could not make seeds would not be a loser on that account. Especially for forms sending out runners, making offsets, or otherwise spreading laterally by parts that will form roots and eventually become effectively or literally independent, the ability for those individuals to do so means they are prospering enough that they can invest more of their excess resources that are not essential right now in these new tissues.

The advantage to us and the long term disadvantage to the species when growing wild is that, except for those one-in-a-million new mutations, all the individuals are genetically identical and therefore susceptible to the same environmental limits. Such a group of genetically similar (they need not be absolutely identical) plants are called a clone whether they form in Nature or only with our intervention. As long as they can be vegetatively propagated as needed their exact traits of flower color, fruit size, growth pattern, disease resistance or whatever can be maintained indefinitely (with a nod to the fact that an occasional new mutant will appear among them but those can be weeded out). This benefits us by allowing us to produce thousands of plants of a named rose variety will full confidence they will all produce the same color flowers and a genetic fluke like a branch of an orange tree that yields seedless fruit can be propagated into whole orchards yielding those fruits. The Bartlett pear was discovered as a chance seedling with better fruit than its relatives about 1770 and is still widely grown today. The Delicious apples come from a tree noticed in an Iowa orchard in 1870.

The long term disadvantage to the species is the vulnerability to rapid changes in environmental conditions that exceed the tolerance of all members of the clone and therefore make it extinct. This is precisely what sexual reproduction gave the species some protection against by assuring that there would be individuals with a range of tolerances for the various environmental factors like temperature, moisture, and nutrient requirements within the population to increase the chance that some individuals would survive and thus keep the species alive despite sudden and significant change.

The ability to turn on the sets of genes needed to produce missing organs is referred to as *totipotency* and it is much more a plant than an animal trait. We have learned to chemically induce single cells from various plant parts to grow into new plants under lab conditions, and learned that the ideal cells for the purpose of those of the apical meristem which need the least coaxing. We have had limited success cloning animals but are able in a few species to remove the nucleus from an egg cell and replace it with the one from a mature cell of another individual of the same species and have that egg grow into a genetically identical copy of the nucleus donor. In animals only egg cells seem open to this manipulation.

We are prompted to focus on the other side of the equation too. If the plant can exercise its totipotency under certain conditions, what is going on in the cells the rest of the time that prevents it from happening all the time? It is vitally important that it should not happen most of the time or what we think of as a normal life cycle for the species would not occur and we can envision disaster as a result in many cases. The plants not setting seeds before the weather changes and killed them because they kept reverting to more vegetative growth instead of maturing to the flowering stage would be likely.

Totipotency would seem to require the release from some kind of chemical controls which probably (considering the situation) are the result of cell contacts, if not actual cell-to-cell communications. Also there must be renewed production of specific stimulants and the support of appropriate nutrients and possibly stage-specific growth factors. All of this the result of turning back on specific sets of genes.

In the wild, asexual reproduction is both a safety net and an opportunity for many plant species. If the plant is broken or partly eaten there is the possibility that some of the fragments may be able to regenerate the other parts and keep the gene line going even though most of the original plant is gone. That is turning disaster into a potential opportunity to spread if several bits, with or without the original stem, survive to regrow after the catastrophe. For perennial plants growing amongst the tangled web of stems and leaves the opportunities for seeds to successfully establish new members of the species are very limited but a vigorous individual may be able to extend some stems horizontally rather than in more upright directions, develop roots where they touch the soil amidst their competitors, and send up satellite colonies of stems that can compete for new spots in the sun. Those new growth centers may stay connected or become separated, the result of infiltrating the competition is the same. Species like *Rosa canina* are masters of this strategy.

The basic techniques of grafting were probably known in China at least as early as 1000 B.C. Aristotle (384-322 A.D.) wrote about it as someone familiar with its results. There was a noticeable renewal of interest in it during the Renaissance (1300-1500 A.D.) as it became important in helping to maintain some of the many new plants being introduced to Europe from the far corners of the world by the great explorers.

Some species or varieties root from stem cuttings more easily than others and they are sometimes used as understocks to rapidly multiply a desirable or finicky type or to assure the genetic identity of the scion or top growth by having the selected highly desirable parent contribute the tissue those parts will grow from by grafting. In recent years we have developed tissue culture techniques that allow us to get large numbers of identical plants in a hurry but that is expensive and relatively high tech so we use it mainly for high value crops that cannot be mass produced as cheaply by other means. It is also limited by lack of success in getting many kinds of plants to grow to maturity in this fashion. For cultivated roses we graft most of the hybrids because they are unlikely to breed true from seed and many are not particularly vigorous growers on their own roots. The procedures are simple if labor intensive and yield a high percentage of successful grafts in well-tested methods so it is the economical way to proceed.

Tissue culture cloning allows the rapid propagation of a single desirable plant (of a type for which the cultural requirements have been worked out) into thousands of identical copies in the shortest time and without the problems of inducing seed set, germination, etc. Using a number of similar but not identical plants that reflect some of the diversity of a natural population in a large scale tissue culture system reduces the genetic dangers of having a monoculture, a large number of absolutely identical plants, without losing the advantages of rapid clonal propagation system.

Another advantage of using the cloning system is that it opens up the possibility of screening a large number of plants for useful mutations like heat or cold tolerance, immunity to diseases, or the effects of certain herbicides, by testing only a single cell or a callus (one of the irregular lumps of cells that are usually formed in the first stage of the process). Only those showing real promise would then have to be induced to grow into full plants that could be tested further in the lab and in the field. At the single cell or callus stages the plants can easily and effectively be exposed to mutation-causing chemicals or radiation to increase the statistical likelihood of finding new forms, a small percentage of which might be worth keeping. A major hang-up of the situation is that we know how to increase the number of mutations in a population of cells or plants but we have no idea how to cause specific ones. The remedy, inefficient but better than nothing, is to treat large numbers of cells and devise some way to then screen out the few that might be useful for our purposes. It is easier and, most importantly in the real world, cheaper to screen the cells before growing them up. The whole process can be carried out in one room of a lab rather than in acres of farm fields and take a few weeks any time of the year rather than a whole growing season limited by the calendar. Once those that are grown out show that their desirable traits are still obvious in the whole plants they can be used as the parents for improved strains of the species by normal breeding methods.

There are cases in which seeds with desirable embryos can be produced by normal cross pollination but for one reason or another they do not germinate reliably. Factors as diverse as a genetic incompatibility between the embryo and the ovule tissue surrounding it, or seed coats that are just too tough for the young plant to split open may be responsible. In such cases the desirable plants may be turned out in the lab by cutting the embryos from the seeds and growing them on an artificial medium in a test tube until they are well enough developed to be transferred like normal seedlings to a pot of soil in the greenhouse or a row in the field. This is not a brand new idea but its implementation has been greatly improved as a result of years of trial-and-error searching for the right medium to meet the needs of each type of young plants since they may differ from species to species. I remember stumbling across a journal article in the early 1960s about this "excision of the embryo" concept as a way to speed the first flowering of hybrid irises by a full growing season and being fascinated by the idea.

Embryonic tissue (and often seeds, including apomictic ones of asexual clones) are virus-free so certified non-contaminated plants of things like strawberries can be commercially grown. Gradually in the field the plants acquire viral infections from insects and other sources and these reduce the survival and the productivity of the plants. By replacing the plants with new virus-free ones every few years the farmers can keep financial disaster at bay, although at a cost.

With the arsenal of tissue culture techniques we can get around some of the barriers that Nature has erected to protect the genetic integrity of species that must compete in the wild. The various genetic incompatibility mechanisms both within and between species that prevent the formation of viable hybrid seeds can sometimes be sidestepped by fusing vegetative cells of the different types together in a lab dish. Dr. Peter Carlson demonstrated in the early 1970s that if the cell walls are dissolved off mature cells, leaving what are called *protoplasts* that are now structurally much more like animal cells, these can be induced to join first their protoplasm and then their nucleii. The resulting two-type parent cells are called *chimaeras* after the mythical Greek creature of mixed body parts. Sometimes these cells can then be induced to grow into whole plants with a mix of the traits of the two parents.

Dr. Carlson's first practical demonstration of the usefulness of the process involved fusing two species of tobacco to show that the resistance to a disease caused by a toxin made by a bacteria could be transferred from the first species to the other while retaining many of the desirable traits of the second parent in the offspring. We might note that tobacco was used here because it is the white rat of plant cell and tissue culture work, the species selected for various reasons by the early workers that is used by many of those who do research in the field in later years precisely because it is already somewhat of a known element from all those earlier studies. Each field tends to have a few such species of choice for that same reason.

The large scale production of F1 hybrid seed requires that the two parent strains that are crossed each be "true breeding" or *homozygous* for all of its traits, which means that it has (within statistical limits since it most cases we cannot check every last gene) two copies of the same allelic form of each of its genes. That assures that each of its gametes will have the same set of genes since there are not alternatives within those cells. And that assures that each hybrid cell receives the same group of genes from the pollen parent and from the egg parent as every other hybrid cell so they will all of necessity be the same.

The production of these true breeding parental strains by conventional breeding methods often takes from three to ten years so they are expensive to create and the payoff is substantially delayed for everyone. Once established these parental strains must be maintained themselves from year to year by growing separate self-pollinated groups to provide the seed to grow the stand of the parental types each year that will be cross pollinated to produce the hybrid seed. At least the developer of the strain has exclusive use of them so he controls the market of that particular type of hybrid seed as long as there is a market for it.

With tissue culture techniques it is sometimes possible to induce the pollen cells of a desirable plant to grow into haploid plantlets which can subsequently be chemically treated to cause them to form duplicate copies of their genes and retain them in the cells, thus converting what started out as gametes into homozygous diploid plants ready to enter service as parental strains of F1 hybrids in months instead of years.

Time generally marches on but from the 1970s to today it has been galloping in the area of genetic understanding and consequent manipulation. Today's genetic engineering procedures are beginning to give us even more precise and controllable ways to transfer desirable traits – and only those – between plant species, genera, families, and even between kingdoms as we work at incorporating bacteria genes into plants to overnight give the plants capacities that none of their kind have ever had before. We are also moving genes in the other direction to empower bacteria to synthesize specific desirable molecule types from plants that until now could only be obtained from the plant tissues and then only in small quantities and after difficult and expensive chemical separation processes. The altered bacteria can churn out substantial quantities of the plant chemicals for use in research, medicine, agriculture, or industry.

CHAPTER 15

THIS IS ROSE'S GROWTH AND DEVELOPMENT

Morphogenesis or "shape forming" of any living thing involves growth in the broad sense which is measured as an increase in size or volume (more cells and/or larger cells) or more protoplasm within the existing same size cells (growth in the restricted sense) *plus* differentiation which refers to an increase in specialization of the cells and tissues to do particular jobs more efficiently.

Growth occurs at the levels of the cell, the organ, and the whole plant but growth in the cell is the fundamental level. The sequence repeated over and over in any cellular organisms is cell division followed by the enlargement and differentiation of the cells continuing to maturity at that time. For a plant, growth at the cell level would include an increase in the amount of protoplasm in the cell, an increase in the volume of the cell (which must be compared under constant environmental conditions so as not to be confused by routine changes in turgor), the extension of the cell wall, an increase in the mass of the cell wall (for instance by the formation of secondary wall layers), and an increase in the number of cells. All of these will occur during the growth of a tissue or the whole plant but each may be most noticeable at different times.

Growth at the organ level simply involves the above processes controlled in time and space to get the right cells at the right place. Plant cells grown in tissue culture show the way as they convert from a blob of callus to differentiated organs and whole plants when stimulated by the right chemical growth factors. Growth in normal plants, however, is limited to the meristems, the only tissues that retain the capacity for cell division. We see plant growth at the organ level as one or some combination of three changes: an increase in the number of parts, an increase in the size of the individual parts, or an increase in the distance between the parts.

The mass of dry weight materials increases in cells during growth, all of it additions to the cytoplasm, organelles, or cell walls and all of it transformed by the cells from their food. Assimilation is the cover term for the processes involved in converting food into additional protoplasm or "new yew." This is mainly a matter of converting relatively simply and generally soluble compounds into more complex and usually insoluble ones that are incorporated into the cell structures. Ordinarily growth is permanent and irreversible as long as reasonably normal conditions persist (and starvation is not normal in this sense).

Growth is a coordinated system of subprocesses that are under the joint control of its genes and the local environmental factors. The genome sets limits to the type and extent of development the plant is capable of but the environment casts many deciding votes within those limits. Potato plants are potato plants but, depending on conditions, the same variety may all grow large or stay small, may flower or not, may produce tubers or not. Producing corn ears or rose hips is genetically beyond potato plants but producing tubers is determined by growing conditions despite being genetically possible. When growing under identical conditions corn, potatoes, and roses show the genetic differences between the species.

Growth depends on delicately balanced sets of simultaneous and serial chemical processes. These in turn depend on molecules some of which are produced in the cell and some of which migrate into it, plus various environmental conditions. All of these factors can affect the rate or nature of growth. There are many reactions and many kinds of reactions going on in the cell at any moment and different molecules of the same chemicals can be involved in different reactions simultaneously but side-by-side.

Environmental factors that affect plant growth include the supply of nutrients and water, the quality, quantity and the sequence and duration of light, the available carbon dioxide for photosynthesis, and various negatives like poisons, pathogens, and predators that are the down side of every organism's existence.

Life is characterized by a dynamic balance of many interacting substances. A change in the proportions of any of the protoplasmic constituents may shift the balance so that it favors and thereby sets off chains of reactions that influence additional cascades of events. Any environmental change is likely to affect the chemical processes unequally, shifting the balances and causing further changes just as closing down a section of any major highway for repairs causes major changes in the traffic patterns all over the city. Sometimes substantial changes in certain factors have little effect while tiny changes in others have big results. The buildup of some metabolic by-product may need to reach a threshold level before it shifts a balance but it may then do so substantially and fairly suddenly. A lot of water may drip into an unbalanced pan before the container is full enough for the weight to shift but then it takes only that one final drop to tilt it over and spill out a lot of its contents.

Most plants as a whole can synthesize all the molecule types they need but the root and shoot systems are closely and reciprocally tied together during development with each supplying some materials critical to the other and dependent on some materials supplied by the other, especially control molecules.

It has been suggested that plant growth is an indefinitely continued embryology since the shoots and the roots are basically copies of the epicotyl and the radicle that emerge from the seed whereas in vertebrate animals the adult form is more changed from that of the early development stages. Also in the plant form there can be an indefinite number of branches, each a repeat of the initial pattern, but there are a limited number of major body parts in the animals and those are established early in its development. This idea clearly has something to it since a woody plant adds a new growth ring to its stems and new shoot and root length each year from meristems that *are* continuing embryonic tissues. The danger with the idea is that we will conclude that plants are not finite. Genetic limits on size, shape, and overall mass of most species argue against that. Plants are different from animals but not too different. The continued embryology of the plants is a system of regulated serial developments or events, not an inherently indefinite phenomenon.

In at least some herbaceous Monocot species like many aroids a specific number of leaf primordia form in the bud that will be the entire above ground portion of the plant for the year and then what will become the flower bud forms to terminate the pattern by maturing the terminal meristem. This means that no matter what happens only that number of leaves can form from that bud (and that usually means from that plant for the entire growing season). In the hyacinth (*Endymion non-scripta*) the bud of next year's plant always forms as the axillary bud of the leaf closest to this year's central flower stalk although every leaf has a bud in its axil that theoretically could do the job.

There tends to a characteristic size for each species. What limits are involved? Generally it seems that the growth limits are more genetic than environmental. Generally animals show a determinate pattern in which they grow to a certain adult size then stop adding height or length. Plants tend toward an indeterminate or continuing pattern but there are many necessary qualifications to these generalizations. Reaching a standard size is important for the plant to fit into the species' strategy of how to compete within a community. Of necessity plants show a flexibility about their growth pattern, growing where conditions allow even if that means becoming lopsided or distorted.

Leaves usually have determinate growth but stems may not and roots seldom do. On a flowering shoot the meristem changes from indeterminate to determinate (and death) since the flower is the terminal growth and has a limited life. In various garden perennial species we see the patterns that either the terminal or the side buds become flowers and then die but not both. Species like some of the palms, bromeliads, and bamboo typically bloom once and the plant dies (called the monocarpic pattern) although in some cases it makes a vegetative offset before it succumbs.

Differentiation leads to polarity. The two ends or surfaces in a living system, its root and shoot, are different. This polarity is inherent in the tissue, not an effect caused by gravity, illumination, or other external conditions. The polarity persists through dormant periods, being very stable and hard to reverse. It seems to reflect a polarity in individual cells – which suggests there should be a structural basis for it but that has not been discovered. If the root of a dandelion is cut into several sections each will always produce shoot buds at the top end and roots at the bottom end. A willow stem suspended in moist air produces roots at what was the lower end and shoots at what was the top even if hung upside down.

Morphogenesis reflects the frequency of mitotic divisions in different parts of an organ and the plane of division of those cells. If the cells all divide in one plane the resulting group of cells will form a flat sheet but if they divide randomly in any plane an irregular mass like a tumor will result.

Detailed cytological studies have found many polyploid cells within the mature tissues of plants that have only diploid cells in the meristems. Apparently these chromosome duplications happen during the differentiation phase when the cells replicate their DNA in preparation for a cell division but then do not divide. But not all of the cells are polyploids, not even all of those doing any particular job. And regeneration of the parts if needed seems to be done entirely by the diploid cells. The contiguous diploid and polyploid cells seem to differentiate as a unified group with no indication that the different kinds of cells are necessary or a problem. More things we need to understand better.

Except in the lab the sum total of the food available to a plant cannot exceed the amount produced by photosynthesis (including what is stored in the various body parts) and a major part of that food is used for respiration and cell repair with only the excess available to convert to new protoplasm as growth. During long stretches of its life cycle a perennial woody plant is not accumulating any food reserves and is actually using them up. When Rose is dormant in the winter she continues to have some root growth and all of her live cells still carry on respiration even if at a reduced level. All of that requires energy that has to come from the oxidation of molecules made and stored during the summer. Even the enzymatic conversion of the insoluble stored food to soluble forms for transport to other cells takes energy.

In some species there is a conspicuous progression from juvenile to mature structures. English ivy (*Hedera helix*) is an example of a species that shifts to a different leaf shape and stem growth pattern as it matures to flowering age.

Physical injury with or without a pathogen involved requires that a plant protect its tissues, prevent water loss, and set up physical and chemical barriers to further pathogen invasion. Cell division starts to change the growth pattern in order to close the wound with cork tissue that will keep water in and insects, fungi, and microbes out. We see this reaction in the corky layer that will form on a cut surface of a potato in a day or two.

Abnormal growths occur. Tumors develop in response to particular bacterial and perhaps some other infections and in some plants a variety of swollen growths called galls develop in the leaves or stems in response to stimulation from insect larvae living within the plant tissues. Nodules or swellings develop on the roots of species that cooperate with nitrogen-fixing bacteria for their mutual benefit.

Growth pattern or architecture is the result of the interaction of a number of factors, most of them genetically controlled so they will be the same in most members of a species and often even a genus. The factors include the activity and distribution of terminal and lateral buds and the extent to which any of those buds may develop. The buds may be spread out or grouped together. The resulting branches may stay as short shoots or grow vigorously. They may grow upright or more horizontally. And those patterns are modified by the extent and degree of bud, leaf, and branch abscission. Depending on the species, only dead or compromised branches may absciss or it may be a regular pattern for some or all of the branches to absciss whole or in part at the end of the growing season.

The Monocots like Lily include very many forms but a large percentage of them can be recognized as growing as some variation of a *sympodial* branching pattern in which a side shoot from the base of a stem extends out and grows into a repeat of the original stem, then a side shoot from it grows out and repeats that pattern, and on and on. Dicots are more varied although among the tree forms there are several major patterns recognized, especially *umbrella* trees with a bare stem and all the surviving branches formed at the top even if there are no competitors nearby to shade out the lower branches, the *pyramid* shape of many conifers that retain their lower branches unless they are tightly packed, and the sympodial pattern seen in branches that results when the terminal stem bud aborts at the end of each growing season so one or more lateral buds take over as the leads, resulting in zig-zag shaped rather than straight branches.

Various measures of growth have been used in quantifying it as part of studies. The indices used have included: (1) increase in length of the stem, root, or other organ; (2) increase in the area of leaves; (3) increase in diameter of stem or other organ; (4) increase in volume, especially of fruits; (5) dry weight gain; (6) fresh weight gain. Each has its use but each is a measure of only certain phases or aspects of growth and none of them measures the important qualitative differences. Note that in most studies of plant size dry weight measurements are recorded because the amount of water within the cells can change substantially as the tissue gain or lose tyrgor and that weight of water is not important to what is being studied in most cases even though it is important to the plant which may wilt because of the loss.

Dr. Peter Marchand and his students have pieced together pretty literally a textbook example of life in particular parts of the real world for balsam fir trees (*Abies balsamea*). He found that at high altitudes in North Eastern U.S. and Canada (and in the mountains of Japan were a similar pattern can be observed) the trees grow and die in such predictable patterns that an aerial view shows crescent-shaped bands or "waves" of dead trees – and if the timing could be speeded up the waves would be seen to sweep steadily across the mountains.

Young fir trees get their start in the openings created by one of these areas of dead mature trees. They have plenty of light and the minerals being released after decades of being stored within the wood of the decaying trees more than meet their needs. As the young trees are growing vigorously some of the mature trees at the edges of the wave are succumbing to a combination of environmental features peculiar to these edge areas.

These edges trees, much more than those in the continuous canopy areas, lose part of their new top growth to winter storms that coat them with ice that then breaks off in the wind, taking branches and needles with it. In these same exposed edge areas storms thrash the trees around and literally break off their roots that are growing in loose rocky soil. Both of these losses weaken the plants enough that the fungus *Resinicium bicolor* that usually lives on decaying vegetation on the forest floor attacks the broken roots. The trees respond to this invasion by sacrificing more of the infected roots to keep the fungus from spreading. But the trees already have reduced photosynthesis, because of the top growth lost in storms and they have already lost part of their root system to storm breakage – and it all becomes too much for them and they die.

The young trees have the advantages of being short enough down in their holes in the canopy that the windy storms do not deposit much ice on their foliage so they do not suffer the loss of needles, and there are enough decaying trunks around them to supply all the minerals they need for vigorous growth so they have surplus energy to deal with loss like some broken roots and to fend off fungus invaders. When they are of mature size but positioned within a continuous area of mature live trees the mineral supply may be a problem since they continue to store them in woody tissues and the supply of rotting wood releasing them is reaching a low level but they can still photosynthesize efficiently and do repairs as needed. It is when their neighbors on one side die and they become part of the edge of the next wave through the area that things fall apart.

The specific circumstances here are peculiar to the fir species growing in these areas but the principles have universal application. Turnover of the dead tissues releases the mineral nutrients for the young growth. When the energy supply is sufficient many insults can be dealt with. It is the specific local conditions, what the ecologists call the microclimate, that each organism must deal with, not the general or average conditions in the area. And a weakening due to one factor may make the organism more susceptible to damage by others.

Some open questions about the growth of the plants close to us. What effects does our artificial lighting have on our plants? City trees under streetlights tend to hold their leaves later in the fall. Does this have any long term good or bad effect that can be measured? Are any species thrown off their reproductive cycles by the lack of light cycling? Is this a serious problem? Who said we have all the answers?

CHAPTER 16

THESE ARE ABSCISSION AND DEHISCENCE IN ROSE'S BODY

The shedding of body parts, called *abscission*, plays a complex role in the physiology and thus the survival of plants. The bottom line is that plants can deliberately drop most any body part when it is no longer useful or needed and do so without leaving an open wound. This is a very *plant* thing since with the exception of epidermal structures like hair or feathers animals do not shed whole body parts. Nor do they routinely grow new ones which is the other end of this phenomenon. Because virtually all the typical flowering plant's body parts can be regenerated or replaced at any stage of its maturity (not without trauma and substantial cost in the more extreme cases but the individual survives) they can be maintained on a strict cost-effectiveness basis. As long as the part provides benefits that outweigh the metabolic costs of keeping it in place it will stay but once it is more of a drain than a benefit it will be dropped without recourse to an appeals court.

Abscission normally includes both the separation of parts and the protection of the main plant body. These steps may occur simultaneously or in sequence but in the latter case the preparatory reactions were made in advance.

Because many plant parts are duplicates the loss of some leaves, some flowers, or some roots will not leave the plant in grave danger even in the short term. Because plants tend to grow continually throughout their lives (although not continuously every day of the every year) the parts formed one year will be shaded, squeezed, or otherwise made useless by those formed later so it makes sense to get rid of any unproductive live tissue and to recycle as much of the useful mineral content trapped within it as possible. Because there are always fungi and other microbes as well as invertebrate animals seeking access to the more easily digestible interior tissues of the plant body as well as the practical problem of losing only the parts no longer worth keeping without damaging those that are, it was important that the mechanisms that developed to win the evolutionary race would produce clean cuts at predetermined points and have the wound healing operations geared up in advance.

Fossil evidence suggests that abscission is a very ancient mechanism, probably going back almost to the formation of the first discrete plant organs. Plants have used it as part of their survival strategies whenever and wherever it occurred but have retained some flexibility even within a species, an indication of the genetic basis of the events. These variations are the working matter of plant breeders who can produce strains of garden flowers that do not promptly absciss their flowers when pollinated and fruit trees that do absciss their fruit to make mechanical harvesting effective. Frederick T. Addicott in his fascinating book *Abscission* (Univ. Calif. Press, 1982) notes that the separation of previously attached cells is the distinctive characteristic of abscission so one can argue that the evolution of the process began the very first time that two cells separated. He notes that there are two major thrusts of abscission evolution – first the localization of the process to particular areas of the plant body, and second the development of control systems that regulate the secretion of the enzymes involved in the process.

The fronds or leaf-like parts of ferns and other lower plants as well as those of herbaceous flowering plants usually wither and eventually detach as a result of decay and external forces like the wind or gravity. The leaves of most conifers and the woody flowering species however are generally shed as a result of changes in a specialized transverse abscission zone at the base, often before the leaf tissues actually die.

The abscission zone is where the decisions are made. This is an active process because the cells produce enzymes specifically for the job of softening or destroying tissues so it can only occur in areas of living tissue although parts of what is dropped may already be dead.

This zone is usually evident as a groove or a line of different color or texture at the base of the petiole as soon as the leaf matures. Sooner or later depending on the species the zone usually becomes differentiated into a *protective layer* that is several layers thick on the stem side of the zone and a *separation layer* several cell layers thick on the leaf side. This happens early in the growing season but then there is no further development of the layers. It is in place if it needs to be used as a result of damage to the leaf during the season but will most often only be called to duty at its end. The petiole of an actively growing leaf does not break more easily at the abscission zone than elsewhere but once the leaf goes into senescence that does become the weak spot.

When the time comes, the middle lamella and often the primary walls of the cells of the separation layer swell and become gelatinous as the insoluble calcium pectate is converted into water soluble pectins. The weight of the leaf, the wind, rain, or other forces then breaks the leaf off cleanly along this abscission layer. More or less simultaneously the cells of the protective layer are depositing waterproofing suberin over their cell walls and strengthening those walls with lignin-like substances, often exactly the same materials the species uses in the gum or "sap" it secretes as part of its normal wound healing process. Thus when the leaf detaches there is not an open wound but an already partly sealed spot that will soon be completely sealed and then covered by a dermal cell layer that is continuous with that of the rest of the stem.

The topic of abscission is a large one because leaves, bark, branches, cotyledons, whole flowers or various parts of them, fruits, and seeds all absciss in many species and the reasons and the seasons for dropping specific parts varies.

Today we view abscission as a phenomenon of correlation and homeostasis. Correlation is the reciprocal influence of one organ on another – like the terminal bud inhibiting the growth of the lateral buds. It is common to have prolonged inhibition of the abscission process, often due to the presence and activity of an organ that is farther from the main stem than the abscission zone. This inhibition usually involves keeping the cells in the abscission zone from maturing relative to the surrounding tissues and preventing synthesis of the necessary hormones. It was observations of these phenomena that led to the discovery of the plant hormones.

Homeostasis is a concept given more attention in animals than in plants but it is a vital idea. It notes that living things work at "staying in the same place," maintaining relatively constant internal chemical and physical conditions. So leaf development is balanced with root development and both are affected by the amount and quality of the available light for photosynthesis. We see examples of it among the plants when, for instance, an annual plant makes only a few leaves and flowers under poor conditions but grows lush and covered with flowers under good ones.

Abscission can rapidly bring the parts into balance when needed. If for instance a sizable part of the root mass is destroyed by some trauma the plant will soon drop many of its leaves so as not to lose water faster than the surviving roots can replace it. Then as the roots regrow the shoots will make new leaves, but still paced to the support the roots can give. Roots can and are abscissed as needed but we are less aware of that unless we are checking closely. In some species that set fruit over an extended period, if the early fruit set the later ones will be aborted but if the early flowers fail to set fruit the later ones will be retained so they can.

The balance is not as rigid as in animals, however. We see this when abundant nitrogen in the soil results in lush foliage but few flowers in species like Nasturtiums.

What are the essential factors in producing abscission? The lowering of the auxin levels, an oxygen supply (to allow production of ATP energy), a fuel source of energy (usually carbohydrates), and the genes, nucleic acids, and amino acids to make the hydrolytic enzymes.

Auxin (IAA) is one of the group of hormones that influence abscission of leaves, flowers, and fruits. The general picture is that auxin produced in the leaf or the flower/fruit inhibits the maturing of the abscission layer between them and the stem. When the amount of that hormone drops because the producing tissue is removed, damaged, or becomes senescent the part is likely to be dropped. A major complication of the matter is that auxin being made in the terminal bud of the stem interacts in some not well defined way with that from the detachable part so that sometimes when we expect the part to detach it does not. Synthetic auxins are used to prevent premature fruit drop in some crops.

Extensive studies of leaf senescence in *Coleus blumei* led to the recognition that IAA is essential to the inhibition of the maturing of the cells of the abscission zone at the base of the petiole. A further fact is that younger leaves make more IAA and their petioles transport it to the abscission zone more efficiently. Chemical tracer studies found that as leaves age they make less of the hormone and progressively a larger proportion of the molecules that are synthesized are immobilized by binding to aspartic acid along the transport route down the petiole. So there is a double whammy effect reducing the level of the hormone reaching the abscission zone and therefore removing the inhibition to its maturing and thereby separating the leaf from the stem.

The hormones abscisis acid (ABA) and ethylene (ETH) can have an effect on abscission but they are considered secondary factors. They are present in all of the species studied but their effects can be counteracted by other factors so while they may promote or facilitate the responses they do not seem to be absolutely essential for them.

Each leaf is in competition for water and nutrients with each other leaf and each flower and fruit is similarly in competition with all others of its kind on the plant. The vegetative organs are competing with the reproductive ones. And each plans competes with its neighbors. In the competition some organs serve as nutrient *sources* and others as *sinks* (like teenagers, bottomless pits). And the same organ may shift from one category to the other over time. During its development a leaf is a nutrient sink, receiving continuing inputs of material from the roots, storage areas, and the older leaves. When fully developed the same leaf is a source of carbohydrates which it sends to other parts although it remains a sink for minerals. As it winds down and senesces it becomes a weaker sink for minerals and eventually a source for them and other materials as it ships out usable molecules before it is lost by abscission. After it falls from the plant the leaf will be decomposed by soil microbes and eventually the minerals will be available for use by this or some other plant but the organic molecules will be incorporated into the microbes and eventually all reduces to carbon dioxide, water, and minerals so it will take the photosynthetic plants to return those atoms and small molecules to living material.

Leaves may be dropped because of temperatures that are too high or too low for effective photosynthesis, because they are receiving too little light or water, because they are severely damaged, or in response to changes in daylength that indicate the end of the growing season and the imminent start of dormancy.

We can recognize a number of benefits to leaf abscission. The removal of non-performing leaves whether senescent, damaged, or diseased. The removal of excess foliage from stressed plants as a homeostatic response. The seasonal defoliation as deciduous species go dormant. The recycling of minerals that cannot be translocated from the tissues more directly. Supplying insulation for roots and seeds or seedlings using parts marked for recycling anyway. In a few cases, especially species with fleshy leaves, vegetative propagation is accomplished. In some cases dropping the foliage facilitates pollination and seed dispersal by animals. And often not obvious to us but very obvious to the other plants, allelochemic suppression of competitors by releasing chemical inhibitors from the leaves into the soil.

The benefits of branch abscission include the termination of growth by shoot tip abortion, the development of the species specific architecture in woody species, the removal of excess branch structures or those compromised by damage or disease, and occasionally vegetative propagation.

The abscission of flowers, fruits, or seeds allows the removal of excess, aborted, diseased, or damaged flowers or fruits. Flower parts that have served their purpose and are now using energy but providing no payback are dropped. In many species, for instance, the flower petals will be dropped a predictable number of hours after pollination occurs. And the separation of the seeds from the mature fruit or of the fruit from the plant is essential to seed dispersal.

There are even benefits to the abscission of some bark since it gets rid of epiphytes and parasites while recycling the minerals trapped in now superfluous tissue.

There is a phenomenon called *compensatory growth* in which the loss of some parts may cause those remaining to grow larger. We see this in flowers, where removing the other buds so there is only one flower per stem results in the large football mums, and in fruits where reducing the number of apples on a tree often results in the remaining ones growing extra large (and therefore bringing a premium price from hungry consumers).

The process of abscission is not universal of course. Rose hips do not absciss cleanly. They die back and the stem section becomes weakened but it takes an external force like a feeding animal or a storm to knock them off. And spiny leafed palm species often retain their dead leaves for years. These droop and form a skirt around the stem studded with many large and nasty spines that discourages many mammals from climbing the trees and damaging the terminal bud or the flowers and fruits.

Dehiscence or the splitting open of fruit or anthers is similar but not identical to abscission. In both phenomena there is a breakdown and separation of parenchyma tissue after the middle lamella and cell walls degrade. The differences include the formation of a protective layer in abscission but not in dehiscence where it is not needed, and the much greater importance of mechanical factors in dehiscence.

Fruit dehiscence is the example most noticed with various dry (and a few fleshy) fruits splitting open entirely or opening various doors through which the seeds can get out. The splitting pattern varies greatly among the plants but is usually uniform within a related group and may help identify them. The shrinking resulting from drying is a major mechanism of fruit dehiscence although some fleshy fruits go the opposite way and explode because of a buildup of fluid pressure in the tissues. Anthers dehisce in order to release the pollen but the pollen sacs are almost never dried out at the time.

CHAPTER 17

THESE ARE ROSE'S GROWTH REGULATING CHEMICALS

That plant and animals grow is obvious all around us, *why* they grow and grow in the specific patterns that they do takes some poking around to discover though and we are only partway through the task of unraveling this complex operation. Growth regulators are chemicals that do exactly that – generally effective in fairly small amounts, they activate or inhibit specific processes to stimulate and later to turn down or turn off growth to keep the parts and functions of the plant in balance.

A clear indication that a mass of cells is a multicellular organism and not just an aggregate of completely independent unicellular types is the production of chemicals by one group of cells that travel to and affect those in other parts of the mass that is therefore a body. Once we grasp that all living things are complicated chemical systems it seems obvious that the signals that control growth and other plant-wide activities will be chemical ones but that does little to identify them. The category of Plant Growth Regulators includes the hormones plus some natural products that do not have hormonal traits and various synthetic materials that mimic the natural molecules.

Like the directly comparable animal hormones, the plant hormones have a set of general characteristics in common. They are always made in one area but affect some other body part. Each molecule has only a short-term effect so that the hormone must be produced continuously as long as the effect is desired. This allows the response to be turned off as well as turned on. They are specific for target tissues since they attach to particular receptors on the outside of the cells. This allows them to be spread throughout the body but only affect the target cells or organs. And they are effective in tiny amounts because they stimulate other reactions but are not major reactants themselves.

The tinyness of the amounts of some chemical materials that will produce a measurable effect on a living system is hard to grasp because the reality of how small and how numerous molecules are defies easy imagining. Chemists routinely measure substance in terms of parts per million (PPM) and parts per billion (PPB) which makes it easy to talk about but also easy to miss the point. A PPM is the equivalent of the amount of chemical in a sugar cube (which is about one cubic centimeter in volume) dispersed through the space of a typical two story, four bedroom house (which is about 1000 cubic meters in volume). A PPB is that same sugar cube dispersed through a thousand of those houses. The growing tip of a pineapple plant (*Ananas*) makes about six micrograms of auxin per kilogram of plant weight, equivalent to the weight of one sewing needle in a twenty-two ton haystack.

The name hormone comes from the Greek word meaning *to excite* because most of the observed effects of those we have identified are increases in some activity level. When inhibitory substances were discovered there was debate about whether they needed a different name but ultimately since they had the same overall general traits listed above they were included in the category.

Hormones are naturally produced growth control chemicals, not substances produced because of or only in response to pathology. We have been able to synthesize many of them and produce chemical variations on them that also have some biological effect.

Among the advantages of hormone control in plants is that it somewhat centralizes the controls although not as much as in animals since each growing tip or other body part may produce some. This "distancing" because a different part makes the hormone than responds to it provides some assurance that the overall condition of the plant will provide vital feedback to speed up or slow down the growth processes.

Hormone are specific but only to a point. Much of our trouble in using hormones to produce desired effects in plants and in ourselves is that the molecule types may do more things than our studies have revealed. The effects of a growth regulator may vary substantially between species or even between different varieties of a species. And even in the same variety each hormone produces a number of physiological responses and several of these responses to different hormones are similar, plus the effect may be influenced by the age, environmental conditions, natural hormonal content, and state of nutrition of the individual plant. Releasing a hormone into a plant or animal body is somewhat like putting a coin into black box vending machine. This may get you a newspaper, a record played on a jukebox, or a candy bar. The coin (= hormone) is less important than the machine (= target tissue and its chemical environment). Growth regulators may increase a plant's resistance to pests or to environmental factors like temperature, water, and air pollution. They may even influence the mineral uptake from the soil or change the timing of a crop's development.

Different plant hormones have various effects on metabolism and cell division. They stimulate cell division in the cambium and the elongation of individual cells in growing parts. They initiate the formation of new roots, especially adventitious ones (those that normally do not occur at those spots). They initiate the development of flowers and of fruit from the flowers. They induce or inhibit the development of lateral buds. They stimulate or inhibit the formation of abscission regions and therefore cause or prevent the dropping of leaves and fruit. Sometimes hormones are used by us to delay the flowering of one variety to synchronize it with another so they can be crossbred and in some cases synthetic hormones will prevent a variety's pollen from forming so it can be the female parent of F1 hybrids in the field.

An important lesson we have learned about chemical controls is not to rule out the possibility that there are other not yet identified materials that may have some effect. Small, commonly present molecule types in particular we tend to assume are not important in plant growth regulation but ethylene has proved that idea wrong so we proceed more cautiously now.

We have also learned the important lessons that the quantity of the hormone is critical and too much is often more disastrous than too little. Plus the timing of the release of the hormone is critical. The cells must be mature enough to respond but beyond a certain point (often when their secondary cell walls start to form) they may no longer be physically able to respond.

A rather simple experiment described by Johannes van Overbeek, one of the big names in growth regulator research, dramatically demonstrates both the selective effects of different hormones and how small a dose it takes to produce a noticeable effect. Seedlings of a bush variety of snap bean were used as the test subjects. A seedling was cut off and trimmed so it consisted of the upper stem portion with two axillary buds and a single leaf. The cut stem was placed in water that contained one PPB of the hormone gibberellin. In a week the plant had only as much new root formation as similar cuttings placed in plain water but, unlike those, its buds had not just swollen but had already developed into the long vinelike stems that are seen in pole beans but not normally in the bush varieties. The conclusion is that gibberellin stimulates stem growth. A similar cutting was placed in a solution of 1 PPM of auxin and in a week had no more top growth than controls in plain water but had a virtual brush of new roots all around its stem. The conclusion in this case is that auxins stimulate root growth.

The researchers started off with the expectation that there would be separate chemicals that would regulate the growth of each major plant body part but as the evidence accumulated this was modified to correspond to the experimental evidence. Today we know that growth and differentiation in plants result from the interplay between various growth factors all of which may affect each part and it is the balance between the control molecule types that determines the growth responses.

We have identified five major groups of growth regulators.

A) *Auxins*. Indole-3-acetic acid (IAA) is the only confirmed natural form but many synthetics have been made that have the same effects. The name comes from the Greek *auxein*, "to increase." These are generally growth stimulators and are the main chemicals responsible for apical dominance.

Auxin is produced in young leaves but does not seem to affect leaf growth rate. It moves slowly from the shoot tips to the root but is not controlled by gravity. The molecules are in solution and will not settle out.

The amount of auxin correlates with abscission, less auxin leads to leaf and fruit drop. Commercial growers of apples and citrus spray orchards with synthetic auxins to keep ripe fruit on the tree until it is harvested. Here the hormonal nature of the control is important because the spray need not hit every fruit since it travels through the tree tissues.

Auxin affects fruit growth. If there is no pollination most species will not develop the fruit. In some cases a single seed per fruit where there would usually be several is sufficient to stimulate the growth, although melons and apples need to have several seeds or they abort. Spraying grapes and tomatoes with synthetic auxins produces seedless parthenocarpic fruit. It is essential that the seeds form on strawberries or the surrounding area of fruit will not develop.

Auxin affects cell differentiation and is needed to form vascular tissue and to induce the growth of vascular cambium to make secondary xylem and phloem in spring when buds sprout.

IAA causes shoots to elongate which is the major mode of plant increase in size. It does this by weakening the cell walls and promoting water uptake but the exact process is complicated and not yet fully understood. Somehow it increases the plasticity of cell walls and thereby permits fluid pressure to stretch them. The hormone also increases the production of the enzyme cellulase to digest some cellulose and weaken the walls. Cut off the growing tip of the shoot and the elongation stops. Add IAA and elongation starts again but usually at a lower rate than in an intact plant. IAA applied to an intact plant, however, produces no observable effect apparently because the plant makes all the IAA it can respond to itself. There are new synthetic products that counteract the effect of IAA and thus keep stems short so holiday mums and poinsettias are compact and better ornamentals.

Auxins promote root and shoot growth in low concentration (5000 PPM) but inhibit it in higher concentrations – therefore use only a dusting of Rootone (which is a synthetic auxin and dilute to start with) on cuttings for best effect. Treatment of potatoes with synthetic auxins inhibits them from forming buds and sprouting.

Like many physiologically active substances the auxins are toxic at high concentration. This is the basis of the use of the synthetic auxin, 2, 4-D as an herbicide. This variaton on IAA retains its activity longer than the natural hormone and, due to variations in the specific receptor molecules (the kind of thing responsible for the variable effects of the same active molecule of any type on different species and even different individuals within a species) it tends to cause some major broad-leafed weed types to literally grow themselves to death while having little effect on the grass, and therefore grain, species because they inactivate it within their cells.

B) *Cytokinins*. These are growth stimulators. The first one was identified in 1955 during research to induce bits of plant in tissue culture to grow into entire plants. More than 100 natural forms have now been identified.

Cytokinins are derivatives of adenine, the same structure involved in DNA, RNA, ATP and other critical molecule types. The hormone is essentially a breakdown product of nucleic acids.

The cytokinins are formed in the root and translocated upwards. They interact with auxins to produce the growth responses, most specifically by stimulating cell divisions. They prevent senescence in leaves by stimulating protein synthesis and have a major effect on the morphology of plants grown in tissue culture. Application to the stem causes some development of lateral buds, opposing the inhibitory effects of auxin although the reaction is not as strong as the removal of the terminal bud.

C) *Gibberellins*. These are growth promoters that mainly cause shoot elongation. They were discovered by Japanese scientists studying "foolish seedling" disease in rice that turned out to be caused by the funguses *Gibberella fujikuroi* and *Fusarium maniliforme*.

They cause stem elongation, promote growth in diameter, stimulate seed germination, induce or inhibit flowering depending on the species and the concentration, retard root growth, break a dormancy cycle, aid fruit production, cause prone plants to grow more upright, and promote increased leaf area. Applications of synthetic gibberellins can cause parthenocarpic fruit in apples, currants, cucumbers, and eggplant. They also cause seedless fruit in mandarin orange, almond, and peach which auxin will not.

Many annual vegetables such as lettuce and dill which normally bloom only when days are long can be made to flower early by gibberellin. Many biennial vegetables like carrots and cabbage which normally need a period of cold temperature to flower will also do so after treatment with gibberellin which can save valuable time in producing seed crops for genetic improvement work and then for commercial seed production.

There are substances known that inhibit either the synthesis or the effects of the gibberellins. The commercial application of such materials produces grain plants with shorter, thicker stems that are less likely to *lodge* or be blown over by wind or rain and have the grains lost in the mud.

The gibberellins play a role in the change from juvenile to adult features. In English ivy (*Hedera helix*) there is a leaf shape difference between adult and juvenile stems and mature stems will not produce roots but do produce flowers while juvenile stems make roots but not flowers. If a mature stem has the apical meristem removed the axillary buds will produce new mature type stems unless gibberellin is applied when they will make juvenile type stems. In *Eucalyptus globulus* the mature stem forms leaves that spiral around the stem, are hard to the touch, and hang vertically but juvenile stems produce leaves that are opposite, soft, and held horizontal or parallel to the ground.

D) *Growth Inhibitors*. This classification includes a variety of materials but the most studied and the main one with hormone type activity is Abscisic acid (ABA), also called abscission and originally called *dormin*. The proper chemical name for the molecule is 2-cyclohexene-1-penta-2,4-dienoic acid, 1-hydroxy-beta,2,6,6,-tetramethyl-4-oxo,cis-2-trans-4-(d). The short name abscissic acid (and the acronym ABA) was applied by the International Conference on Plant Growth Substances held in Ottawa in 1967 to simplify discussion. (Thank goodness!)

Under adverse conditions it induces a resting bud and stimulates the plant to develop resistance to stress in various ways including the promotion of dormancy. In many species it stimulates leaf abscission although it is not essential to that process and the name is now recognized as being misleading.

ABA blocks the action of auxins, gibberellins, and cytokinins and thus inhibits growth or regulates it in combination with those various stimulators. There are very high levels of ABA in buds in the fall to keep them dormant as the leaves absciss. It shows little effect on dwarf plants but a significant effect on normal sized ones.

The Duckweeds, some thirty species of tiny floating plants in six genera, are the smallest and simplest of the flowering plants. They are also very sensitive to ABA which makes them good as study subjects of the effect of this hormone. As little as 1 PPB in the water measurably slows the growth of these species and 1 PPM puts them into dormancy indefinitely. Yet the effect is quickly reversed once the hormone is removed.

Researchers found they could turn the growth of Duckweed on and off virtually at will with hormones. Adding 1 PPM of ABA to the water of a dish of rapidly growing plants (and Duckweed multiplies rapidly under good conditions, some types able to vegetatively double the number of plants every three days) will stop the growth. But then adding one part in ten million of cytokinin to the water causes the growth to resume at the original rate even though the ABA is still present.

We assume this is what happens in nature, that different concentrations of the hormones turn activities on and off. It is revealing that the plant has both accelerators and inhibitors of growth to give fine control the way that both gas pedal and brake do when we drive a car. So the start of bud growth in spring may be the result of an increase in the amount of auxins, gibberellins and/or cytokinins in those tissues or it may be most directly the result of a decrease in the amount of ABA there. Most likely it is a combination of these general factors and the precise situation is somewhat different from group to group among the many plant species.

Plant cells keep things simple by regulating the first step in the sequence of events that result in growth. Auxin and cytokinins increase nucleic acid synthesis and ABA decreases it. The formation of the three groups of RNAs is a necessary prelude to the synthesis of proteins (or any other molecule types not already being made within the cell at that moment which will require proteins for their production). The nucleic acid synthesis is the logical place to turn the whole process on or off since if it were halted at some midway point there would be a potential problem of the early products of the sequence piling up or other chemical machinery being needed to somehow store, dismantle, or otherwise dispose of those, plus the inevitable waste of energy involved in all those reactions.

E) *Ethylene* (ETH). This is the oddball hormone because it is released and has its effect as a gas rather than traveling dissolved in the fluids moving within the plant. It has several identified activities. Generally it mediates growth inhibition.

Ethylene plays a role in fruit ripening and the stimulation of abscission. High levels may produce *epinasty* in which the top of the petioles grows faster than the bottom which makes the leaves bend over as if dropping while stay firm and functional.

During fruit ripening there is a large intake of oxygen along with the production of ethylene so putting some fruits in plastic bags slows their ripening by limiting the oxygen available to them.

This gas is associated with touch effects. Rubbing or shaking plants generates it and leads to stunting as is often seen in seaside or mountaintop plants that are regularly buffeted by the wind. The salt spray, cold temperatures, etc. contribute to the stunting but greenhouse studies suggest that the movement of the plants is a critical part of it.

The effects of ethylene were known long before the chemical responsible for them was identified because the techniques to study gases in plants were only developed in the 1950s. Experience had taught, for instance, that a company should not transport oranges and bananas in the same ship or the bananas will arrive overripe and spoiled. We find a variation on that ship's hold put to practical use to induce flowering in many bromeliad species. The standard advice is to close the mature bromeliad in a plastic bag with an apple or an orange for a few days and several weeks later the bromeliad will be in bloom, stimulated by the ethylene given off by the fruit.

The interactions of the plant hormones and other factors like phytochrome is recognized and seen to be complex and so far only partly understood. The interaction between ethylene and auxins is typical of the problems. Auxins generally stimulate the production of ethylene gas so many of the effects that we think are caused by the auxins may actually be the direct effects of ethylene. The analysis of this is further complicated by the fact that exposure to ethylene gas stimulates the plant to make and release even more of the gas itself.

Phytochrome is not a hormone because it does not pass between cells or tissues but it is critical to the regulation of many growth processes because it is involved in daylight detection and photoperiodism. We will consider it more in **Chapter 18**.

Other natural organic molecules that affect plant development at low concentrations are known, including triacontanol, brassinolide, and a cryptochrome blue light detector. Some volatile chemicals like xylene present in paints may cause blasting of buds in Mums or bud drop in roses. Similarly methane or natural gas will damage some species.

CHAPTER 18

THESE ARE ROSE'S PIGMENTS

Our world is full of colors and that is no accident. Three hundred years ago Sir Isaac Newton demonstrated that visible "white" light, ordinary sunlight, can be spread out to reveal itself to be a rainbow of separate component wavelengths or colors by passing it through a glass prism (or water droplets in the air that make the rainbow in the sky) where each wavelength is bent to a different degree. So color is inherent in visible light itself. The colors of the objects around us result when white light strikes them and their molecules absorb some wavelengths and transmit or reflect others. It is those light rays that bounced off or passed through the object that can then reach our eyes and since they only contain the colors not absorbed we perceive the object as being the colors it does not absorb.

The physicists tell us that *quanta* or tiny indivisible units of radiant energy travel in light, with the amount of energy per quantum varying inversely with the wavelength. That means that shorter wavelengths (x-ray, ultraviolet, and into the visible violets and blues) contain more energy than long ones (reds, fading through the infra-reds into the radio frequencies). Is it a coincidence that the biological activities that depend on radiant energy all use wavelengths within the band of the electromagnetic spectrum that correspond to our visual range? Dr. George Wald, an expert on the subject of life and light, argues that it could not be otherwise.

His reasoning is that since living things depend of macromolecule types that are held into critical 3-D shapes by weak hydrogen bonds, wavelengths only slightly shorter than violet light are too violently disruptive for the tissues to tolerate because they break apart those bonds, while wavelengths longer that red are too low energy for most plants to harness because they cannot excite electrons to higher energy levels, an effect essential to many biological changes. This is why what is visible light to us is that narrow range of wavelengths. Our retinal cells could not derive enough energy to react to weaker wavelengths or survive the impact of stronger ones.

He also believes that if there is life elsewhere in the universe those forms will use the same part of the spectrum for their energy conversion processes. This he says is because that part of the EM spectrum is what is available to living things. Life as we can conceive of it requires certain environmental conditions and one of those is a suitable atmosphere. Water, ozone, carbon dioxide, and other atmospheric gases absorb and thus filter out much of both the higher energy and lower energy wavelengths before they reach the surface of the planet so what radiant energy forms are available to plants is limited.

Pigments are molecule types that appear colored to us because they absorb light of specific wavelengths and therefore transmit or reflect a particular range of wavelengths. For our purposes there are two groups of pigments, those that are momentarily changed by the absorption of the light energy in a way that contributes to a physiological response, and those that produce colors that are useful to the plant directly because of their signal value to animals. The chlorophylls are a prime example of the first group, the anthocyanin pigments that accumulate as a signal of fruit ripening the second group.

In plants pigments are critical parts of the machinery of photosynthesis (the chlorophylls and carotenoids), cell respiration (the cytochromes), and cyclic and seasonal responses (phytochrome). Some of the carotenoids plus a variety of other pigment types are used for protection from dangerous UV radiation and from predators as camouflage, to attract animals for various purposes, or as a *Don't Touch* warning to animals. It seems obvious that at least many of the attractant colors are produced for that effect because they are only accumulated when the plant needs the animal cooperators. There are occasional examples of colors that seem to us to offer the plant no advantage or that even make it harder for them to photosynthesize and survive but the continued existence of such species makes us wonder if we are missing something and these are actually some clever physiological trick by the plants.

We should make special note of the contribution of plant pigments to animal vision. Our visual sense depends on carotenoid molecules that no animal can synthesize on its own. We all must obtain versions of these molecules pre-formed as vitamin A from the tissues of plants or animals (which obtained them from plants) in our diet. Your mother was right that if you don't eat your carrots or other veggies you won't have good vision, especially not good night vision. So the plants make the colors and also enable us to see them.

The pigment types that are essential to physiological processes are ones that temporarily change their shape when they absorb light energy of specific wavelengths. In doing so they either fit into a critical step in an energy conversion process or they are shifted from one pile to the other in a timing process. The fact that the molecules are reusable because they can be switched back and forth between the forms repeatedly over time makes the system that much more efficient.

Green is the predominant color in plants because it is the color of the chlorophylls, plural because there are two slightly different but equally important molecule types in flowering plants, designated *a* and *b*, and other forms in lower plants and bacteria. These absorb light in the red and the blue areas of the spectrum. Chlorophyll *a* is the only molecule type that can feed light energy into the photosynthetic molecular machinery.

In a test tube chlorophyll molecules absorb light and some electrons are raised to a higher energy level and then they fluoresce as those electrons drop back to the lower energy level and the energy is reemitted as light of a longer wavelength. By themselves the pigment molecules cannot store the energy. Only when they are part of a photosynthetic unit in a chloroplast can they pass those high energy electrons along to other molecules that can funnel the energy into molecular bonds rather than releasing it immediately as light.

Accessory pigments are ones that also collect energy but must pass it to the chlorophyll *a* molecule to get it into the photosynthetic machinery. These include chlorophyll *b,* some of the carotenoid pigments, and in some algae and bacteria a class called the phycobilins. Since each pigment absorbs particular groups of wavelengths a combination of accessory pigments allows more of the solar energy to be captured and stored.

The carotenoids are red, orange, or yellow fat soluble pigments some of which are found in all chloroplasts and some also found in other cells at specific times. It is specifically two subgroups, the carotene and the xanthophyll pigments, that are found in all chloroplasts where they are accessory pigments that assist the chlorophyll but cannot substitute for it. In green tissue the carotenoids are simply being hidden by the large amounts of chlorophylls present. When the leaves senesce typically they change to reddish or orange-brown shades for a time as the chlorophylls decompose leaving the other pigments revealed. Beta carotene is the principal source of vitamin A that we need to get from plants.

The cytochromes are molecule types that do high energy electron transfers very similar to those done by the chlorophylls so not surprisingly they have very similar structures. These are not pigments that we ever see except in the lab because they are present in only very small amounts but they are present in virtually every living cell in the plant (or animal) body. Several different ones are among the components of the electron transport chains that make energy from high energy electrons available to produce ATP energy transfer molecules both in cell respiration and in photosynthesis.

If they remain active most vegetative buds eventually change into flower buds. Why that happens and may happen to one stem of a plant but not a similar one on the same plant under experimental conditions is a major question of botany. In the second decade of this century Americans H.A. Allard and W.W. Garner, working for the U.S.D.A. and putting our tax dollars to good use, showed that a major environmental factor in inducing flowering in many species is the photoperiod or daylength.

Their work was highly practical. They were hired to find ways to improve soybeans as an oilseed crop. They noted that if the Biloxi soybean variety was sown in the field at intervals across the spring and summer all bloomed at about the same time and careful greenhouse studies proved that neither the intensity nor the spectral quality of the light was responsible. They were also examining Maryland Mammoth tobacco, a mutant that grew very large in the field because it did not go to flower there but did so if brought into the greenhouse or even sown there in winter. Eventually they showed that both the soybeans and the tobacco flowered when the daylength was shorter than a specific interval, that length varying between species and even varieties.

Many others then focused on the effect of daylength and soon recognized that it was actually the length of the night that was critical since it is interruption of the dark phase by light not the other way around that sets the clock back to the starting point. Today we know there are long-day (or short-night) plants that need a continuous dark period of *less* than a genetically-determined length, short-day (or long-night) plants that require a continuous dark period of *more* than a certain minimal length, and day-neutral plants in which the daylength does not seem to be an important factor in the timing of flowering.

The practical payoff of this recognition of photoperiodism is that we can get mums, poinsettias, etc. to flower for any holiday period of the year, and can make practical decisions about which varieties of grains to grow where in order to assure a crop. The theoretical consequence was to set researchers off on the quest for the molecular mechanism that made it happen. And that led to the discovery of *phytochrome* or "plant color".

Phytochrome is an enzymatic pigment involved in daylight detection, photoperiodism, and probably some circadian rhythmic responses in plants. It was isolated and named by a U.S.D.A. group in 1959 after 25 years of work led them through the sequence of conclusions that natural light was a critical factor, the length of the light exposure rather than the quality of the light was the important factor, and that there had to be a single molecule type involved that could change its shape in response to light of specific wavelength.

Phytochrome is not a hormone because it does not pass between cells or tissues. Its oh so useful trick is that, as predicted, it has two interconvertible molecular forms, one designated *Pr* that absorbs red light (660 nm) and one designated *Pfr* that absorbs far red light (730nm). In 1966 it was shown to be chemically allied to the phycobilins, a class of pigments found in some algae that have an open-chain tetrapyrrole (a pyrrole is a type of ring of carbon and nitrogen atoms) as a prosthetic group tightly bound to a protein. The significance of this is that it is the prosthetic group that actually changes the position of two hydrogen atoms to alter its shape when exposed to the red or far-red light.

In U.S.D.A. studies it became evident that red light and far red light had opposite effects on a wide range of plant-growth processes and, quite significantly, the effect can be reversed back and forth any number of times simply by changing from one wavelength to the other and all these reverses do not harm the physiological systems.

Pfr, the form most sensitive to far red light as a result of exposure to red light, is the metabolically active form of phytochrome. The Pr form absorbs light more effectively than the Pfr form so the mix of wavelengths in sunlight converts most of the phytochrome in the cells to the Pfr form. In darkness Pfr tends to revert at a steady rate to the Pr form. And that is what makes it a light detection system that can measure daylength and explain why it is the continuous dark period that is actually the critical parameter. Things happen depending on the level of Pr and that is increasing the longer the darkness continues.

That the effects of Pfr are genetic based is evident from the fact that the molecule tends to promote some growth responses and inhibit others and it may have opposite effects in different species. It promotes the flowering of long-day plants but inhibits the flowering of short-day types. Pfr promotes germination in about half of hundreds of species tested but it clearly inhibits the sprouting of some types. In general it promotes the expansion of leaves and the unbending of the hypocotyl hook during seedling emergence. *Etiolation*, the excessive stretching of newly emerged seedlings kept in the dark is a direct result of lack of sufficient Pfr. The influence of the phytochrome on growth is modified by environmental and hormonal factors.

The "appearance" colors used in petals, fruits, and sometimes bracts or selected leaves as signals to animals fall into several chemical groups that accumulate in different parts of the cells.

Many of the red, orange, and yellow shades come from fat-soluble carotenoids present in chromoplasts in the cytoplasm. Others come from tiny insoluble particles of scarlet through magenta anthoxanthin pigments, or water-soluble pale ivory through yellow anthocyanin pigments, both contained within the central vacuole of the cell. Specific cell wall components may add some red or yellow tones.

Some orange shades result from orange colored carotenoid pigments while others, like those in Nasturtium petals, result from a red cell sap and a yellow plastic pigment within the same cells. The combination of a yellow sap and red plastids is less common but also is found in some species.

Purples and blues can be from anthocyanin pigments, anthocyanin-anthoxanthin co-pigmentation, or from tricky reflections of the light without a true pigment present. There are also specific blue or purple cell wall materials. There is a rare blue-green pigment called xylindeine from European wood rotting fungus *Chlorosplenium aeruginescens*.

Some bluish appearances are the result of hairs or waxy scales on the surface that make them *glaucous* by the way they reflect light. The electric blue leaves of some deep shade plants like *Selaginella uncinata* and sedges of the genus *Maparia* are iridescent, their peacock blue appearance a combination of greens resulting from the reflection of diffuse light onto specially oriented chloroplasts by special lens-shaped cells and blues resulting from thin film interference filters in the leaf epidermis. For us it produces a stunning color, for the plant it allows better absorption of red wavelengths in deep shade.

Green pigment other than chlorophyll are rare but there is one called verdigris green in the petals of the South African corn lily *Ixia virififlora*.

Brown into black shades are derived from several sources. Most are cell wall colors, as we see in many fern fronds and some orchid flowers. Some brown pigment molecules only form when tissues are oxidized after being damaged, like a cut apple. There is a brown plastid pigment in broomrape (*Orobanche*) and the birds-nest orchid (*Neottia nidus-avis*). There is a brown cell sap pigment in *Coelogyne* orchids and some *Delphinium* petals and sepals. Or the color may result from the combination of other colors, like red cell sap plus green chloroplasts in the same cell or in separate overlying layers of cells. In swamp species it can even be the result of a crust of iron oxide on the leaves.

White colors may be due to white anthoxanthin pigments in the cell sap or to reflection and refraction of light in air spaces within the tissues just as ice with no air in it is clear but the mix of air and ice makes snow appear white. In some cases light reflection from surface hairs makes leaves look white.

Ultraviolet light that is important to the navigation of bees and other insects is a reflection phenomenon, not a pigment, although some pigments *absorb* UV light.

Rose flower colors come from various combinations of the pigments of the classes described above with breeders constantly mixing the gene pot and trying for new shades or combinations.

Variegation, a mix of two or more colors in the leaves or stems, is usually the result of spotty production of the various standard pigments. It may be caused by an increase or a decrease in the number of particular types of plastids in the cells or by defective ones without a change in their number. White or yellowish variegation is most common and this requires no additional pigment. White areas simply show a total absence of pigment or the presence of air spaces within the tissue, or some combination of these. Variegation yellows are usually the result of reduced amounts of chlorophyll rather than of any additional yellow pigments but there are many exceptions. Silver variegations are caused by surface reflectors like special waxes and/or air spaces within the tissue.

Sun loving types tend to lose their variegation if grown in the shade because they tend to increase their photosynthesis tissue to compensate for the reduced light availability, while shade loving types tend to lose it in sun.

Variegation may occur as a result of a viral infection, a mineral deficiency (in which case it will disappear if that need is met), changes in the leaf structure that result in air spaces or areas of unusually thin epidermis, chimaeras in which different leaf cell layers have different genes operative, or genetic changes like somatic mutations or chromosomal aberrations.

Darker and lighter areas of the same color in petals usually result from different concentrations of either the pigment in the chromoplasts, of chromoplasts in the cells, or of cells with chromoplasts among those that lack them. The presence of air spaces in the tissue will also result in a lighter color.

CHAPTER 19

THESE ARE ROSE'S SCENTS

For roses more than other domesticated plants their long history in cultivation with man has been closely associated with their scents. For centuries the highly scented blossoms have been important as symbols of love and widely grown for medicinal purposes. To extend the season of their availability they were used to make rose water, potpourris, and perfumes that provided both pleasure and an important economic impact (which also brought smiles to many faces all those years).

Humans have used selected scents derived from plant flowers, leaves, roots, woods, and gums since the dawn of history to flavor foods and beverages, as religious and love offerings, to cover body odor, to tuck between bed linens, or to strew around the house to mask unpleasant odors as their scents were released by being walked on. At some point it was recognized that they also helped to keep away irritating and disease carrying bugs. In recent years aroma therapy has reemerged as a New Age fascination, continuing the trend.

Presumably scents originated with volatile substances the plants produced as by-products of some chemical processes and were simply allowed to evaporate away because they were not needed or were even dangerous. When some of these proved useful natural selection favored the individuals with the genes for making these substances and they became a standard part of the species' repertoire. Some attracted animals that pollinated the plant or dispersed its seeds. Some repelled predators or warned off animals that might have eaten it only to discover it contained poisons. And some gave protection against fungal or bacterial infections. Many of these volatile chemicals are effective precisely because of their odor or taste but those qualities are only incidental to the antimicrobial effects.

We have a relatively poor vocabulary for scents which makes it hard to describe or even categorize them objectively. Probably because of the close association of our smell and taste sense many of our descriptive names for scents are food references – lemon, raspberry, almond, coconut, and so on. The descriptive process is further complicated by great individual differences in both sensitivity to and reaction to many scents. At least in part due to genetics, some people pick up even small traces of an scent but others need it much stronger to detect it. Also some hate what others find delightful but this may have more to do with personal experiences unconsciously associated with the odors than any biological factors.

Scents serve a purpose for the plant and the purpose to be served or the animal cooperator to be attracted determine what scent will be effective. In his *Scented Flora of the World* (St. Martin's Press, 1977) Roy Genders describes ten flower fragrance groups, some pleasant to human noses and some not.

01) *Indoloid* flowers contain abundant indole, an odor characteristic of animal decomposition. Species like the *Stapelias*, relatives of the milkweeds, come as an unpleasant surprise to the unprepared when one opens its large starfish-shaped flower and starts to smell like a dead animal since it evolved to attract carrion flies, not houseplant blue ribbons.

02) *Aminoid* flowers like Pyracanthra and Privet contain triethylamine, the odor of fish brine and a characteristic smell of early putrefaction, and reek of ammonia. These flowers also are trying to attract flies as pollinators.

03) The *heavy scent* group contain some indole but it is mixed with benzylacetate and methyl anthranilate (which is a strong odor of oranges) which cuts the hint of putrefaction unless you sniff honeysuckle, lily of the valley, plumeria, or tuberose too closely.

(04) *Aromatic* flowers contain eugenol, the essential oil involved in cinnamon, clove, vanilla, and balsam odors.

(05) *Violet* flowers contain ionone, a ketone that gives violets, mignonettes, and *Rosa banksiae* their distinctive odor. As it fades it suggests woodland moss or fresh cut cucumbers.

(06) *Rose-scented* flowers contain the alcohol geraniol that is abundant in the leaves of the rose-leaf geranium (*Pelargonium capitatum*) as well as roses and other flowers.

(07) *Lemon* scents result from the aldehyde citral which is the molecule type formed when geraniol is oxidized. It is found in many flower and leaf scents, including *R. bracteata*.

(08) *Fruit-scented* flowers contain esters that make us think of specific fruits like apricots (hybrid tea roses 'Chantre' and 'Andre le Traquer'), oranges (rambler roses 'The Garland' and 'Wedding Day'), green apples (*R. wichuraiana*), or bananas (*R. soulieana*).

(09) *Animal-scented* flowers contain esters of fatty acids. Musk scented roses fit into this group, including the musk rose, *R. moschata*, that releases the musky odor from its flowers and the moss rose, *R. muscosa*, that releases a similar one from glandular hairs on its leaves and flower stems. *Centranthus ruber* is also known as Valerian because it makes valeric acid, a component of human perspiration that can make a large bed of this species smell like a locker room on a hot afternoon.

(10) *Honey-scented* flowers are related to the animal-scented group but the impression is sweeter and specifically of honey.

A few species like Sweet Alyssum (*Lobularia maritima*) have unique flower scents that do not fit well into any of the groups.

Most plant scents come from essential oils. These evaporate more slowly than a water-based material would and so stretch out the perfume effect. They are also more easily stored within the cells than water soluble materials would be.

Floral scents are freely released into the air but those from leaves and other parts may only be released if the leaves are touched or in some cases only if they are handled roughly.

The floral scents come from the oxidation and evaporation into the air of the essential oils from epidermal cells of the petals, or the sepals or bracts that may act as petal substitutes. To assist the process odorous petals are almost always thick and velvety to slow the evaporation of the oil and make the effect last. Experiments done at the turn of the century found that orange blossoms yield different scent components from the upper and lower petal surfaces.

Since it depends on evaporation the odor is often only released when the flower is open and the odor of cold flowers is less obvious because literally it is not coming off the petals. Breathing gently into the flowers on a cold day may make a noticeable difference to your reception of their scent.

Because scent comes from the petals the more petals there are, the more scent. So double forms of scented flowers are usually more strongly perfumed.

Stephen Lacey says in *Scent In Your Garden* (Little, Brown & Co., 1991) that in some roses like the Musk rose (*R. moschata*) the oil is found in the stamens so that double forms which have fewer stamens have less odor.

An odor's strength correlates inversely with its volatility. Those like cedar that are slow to evaporate are *strong* odors and last a long time, while those like citron that evaporate fast and are soon gone are *feeble* odors. Attar of roses is a strong odor. In fact it is unpleasantly overwhelming in concentrated form and there are claims that if inhaled at close range the concentrate may cause brain hemorrhage and death.

The essential oil is stored in the plant cells as glycosides, the lipid molecules bonded to sugars. Genders says that chlorophyll is chemically transformed into tannoid compounds and then into essential oils and that this explains why green flowers are not odorous. It is also correlates with the theory that flowers are modified leaves.

Among wild or only mildly hybridized species there is a rule of thumb that the lighter the flower color, the stronger its scent. At the turn of the century a study found that more than 60% of 4000 types of scented flowers examined were white or light colored and that other colors of the same species tended to have less scent. In many species the pattern has been that as color was bred into hybrids they lost their scent, like Sweet Alyssum variety 'Rosie O'Day' that has rosy-purple flowers but little of the fresh mown hay scent of the typical white forms.

The subtlety of a flower scent is the result of the particular mix of compounds in its essential oil. The most common of the components are esters which are formed when an acid combines with an alcohol (which all have names ending in -ol). For instance acetic acid plus ethyl alcohol produces ethyl acetate that has a distinctly lemony odor. Borneol, that has a piney or turpentine odor, is the chief alcohol found in leaves. There is also menthol, characteristic of the mint family, and linalol, the characteristic odor of the lavenders. Linalol combines with acetic acid to form the ester linalyl acetate that is easily converted into geraniol.

Geraniol is the alcohol that imparts the characteristic pleasantly sweet rose scent. It is "geranium alcohol" rather than "rose alcohol" because one of the best sources of it in relatively pure form is the leaves of the rose leaf geranium although a discriminating nose can tell true attar of roses from that derived from the geranium leaves by subtle overtones of other materials.

It is differing amounts of at least eight other compounds that determine the particulars of the scent of specific rose species or hybrids, with fruity, honey, or spicy overtones. Roses have probably the most varied set of floral perfume groups of any plant genus, with at least seventeen reasonably distinct groups detectable by sensitive noses. As I emphasized in the listing of floral scent types above, rose floral scents may include notes of incense, clove, raspberry, apple, banana, orange, lemon, and the "myrrh' scent that many people describe as a "facial cold cream" odor in several hybrids like 'Constantine Spry' and 'Belle Isis'. However not all of the rose scents are pleasant, especially not in concentrated form. *R. foetida* contributed the yellow flower color to many hybrids but it also gave them stinky flowers as its name suggests because they contain indole that as we noted above is an odor generally associated with decaying flesh.

Attar or *otto* comes from an ancient Persian word for scent or smell and refers to the purified essential oil. In the late tenth century the Arabian doctor Avicenna discovered the method of steam distillation of attar from the petals of the Damask rose and his method for making rose water soon spread widely. An *essence* is the alcohol solution of the essential oil. This is a practical way to extract the oil from the flower petals and concentrate it since oils readily dissolve in alcohol but not in water. This method came into use about 1370 when Queen Elizabeth of Hungary is reported to have produced an essence of rosemary leaves using a recipe obtained from a hermit.

Essence of rosemary became the basis of complex blends of scents used as herbal toilet waters that came to be called *eau de colognes* or "Cologne waters" due to the fame of the products of the brothers J.M. and J.B. Farina after they moved to the city of Cologne from Italy. Many participants in the Seven years War of 1756-1763 took some of these materials that were generally considered to be suitably masculine fragrances home with them from the battles and their fame became widespread.

Many argue that the truest rose scent is epitomized by that of the Damask rose (*R. damascena*), which is a ancient hybrid not a wild species and which gave its name to the Syrian city of Damascus where it is widely grown, not the other way around. Some types of *R. rugosa* seem to have the strongest doses of the main essential component which we now know is the geraniol.

The mixture of materials we detect from a flower can change with the weather conditions and with the life cycle of the plant. Some scents are pleasant in very dilute form but decidedly less so when concentrated. The amount of essential oil present varies considerably from species to species and plant part to plant part. Ten pounds of clove seed will yield about twenty-five ounces of clove oil but ten pounds of orange peel will yield only a single ounce of attar of orange. It takes about 250 pounds of rose petals to yield an ounce of attar of roses.

In 1971 the *Complete Rosarian* published the analysis of the volatile chemicals found in the essential oil extracted from the cabbage rose, *R. centifolia*. The list contains eleven components, three of which account for 90% of the materials – phenylethyl alcohol (50%), Citronellol (30%) and Geraniol (10%). The other ten percent are the little high notes and base notes that a well trained note can distinguish between one variety and another. And the same group of molecule types are used in different combinations and proportions by many species, not a single identified component is unique to roses.

Attar of roses is highly antiseptic. Carbolic acid or phenol was the first material used for the purpose in the operating room by Dr. Lister and remains the official test standard for comparison of antiseptic effectiveness tests even though it is now considered too corrosive for use on the skin. One source reports that attar of roses has seven times the antiseptic strength of phenol while that from garden thyme has twelve times the strength. The caution here is that an antiseptic is deadly to some but usually not all forms of viruses, bacteria, and fungi so strength comparisons need to be understood as suggestive rather than absolute.

Flowers that depend on butterflies, moths, beetles, or bats to pollinate them or disperse their seeds are often scented since all of these animal groups have a good sense of smell so it is no surprise that beetle pollinated species like roses are strongly scented. Bees are visual searchers and rose blossoms do not have much nectar anyway so they are not attracted to them.

A few species of orchids depend on attempted or *pseudo*-copulation by male bees or wasps for pollination. The insects are tricked into mistaking the flower for a female of their species in order to get the contact needed for pollen transfer. Part of the trickery is for each orchid species to emit a scent similar to the mate attraction pheromone used by the particular insect species it depends on since such chemical messages are usually different for each species.

Scents include many from foliage as well as from flowers. In foliage the scented compounds function as antiseptics against microbes and discourage insects and other animal browsers with astringent tastes or outright poisons. The irony is that most of the highly scented and strong tasting materials that we call spices and seek out as cooking ingredients are made by the plants precisely to discourage insects and other animals from eating them. This is also a good place to note that one of the most important developments in human history was the practice of cooking our foods since this neutralizes many of the chemical defenses the plants have acquired over a long evolutionary history. Literally by cooking them we make many otherwise dangerous plant materials into suitable food.

Some scented materials are allelochemic weapons used in the competition with other plants. The aromatic terpenes camphor and cineole evaporating from the leaves of shrubs like *Salvia leucophylla* and the sagebrush *Artemesia californica* in the chaparral regions of the coastal foothills north of Los Angeles give the whole shrub dominated area a characteristic pungent odor. They also prevent the growth of other plants, even grasses, within several feet of the strong smelling bushes because they saturate the top layer of soil and poison any seedlings. The distinct bare zone around them can easily be seen in aerial photos. For a period after one of the periodic fires passes, the grasses grow right up to the charred shrub stems since the terpenes in the soil burned off with the foliage but over the months as the shrubs resprout the bare zone redevelops.

Leaf scents may fit into any of the groups listed for flower odors or into one of four additional groups: camphor or eucalyptus scents, mints that all contain menthol, turpentine-scented species like rosemary that contain a lot of borneol acetate, or sulphur odors found in the mustard and onion groups.

Leaf scents are more likely to come from essential oil with a single component. Eucalyptol gives the herby scent to Eucalyptus leaves as well as those of yarrow. Lemon scent is due to citral, a compound found in the fruits of all citrus and the leaves of many species. Synthetic forms of many of the scent compounds are used in a multitude of products today.

Leaf scents tend to become stronger as the leaves dry because the essential oil becomes more concentrated in the cells as the water content drops – so you need less dried basil leaf than fresh for the same taste impact. The scent of flowers diminishes as the petals age or dry.

In some species the leaf scent is most noticeable immediately after a rain. The incense odor of *Rosa. primula* and the apple odor of *R. eglanteria* are typical examples.

The seeds, wood, bark and/or roots may have a scent, usually due to resinous materials. For the centuries before people learned to distill attars the gums, resins, barks, and woods were the main scented materials of commerce because only they would retain their odor long enough to be shipped long distances.

Some species have more than one scented part. *Rosa setipoda* has scented flowers, leaves, and stems. Allspice, *Calycanthus floridus*, has apple scented leaves but camphor scented wood and roots. Topping that, *Lindera benzoin*, a North American deciduous shrub sometimes called wild allspice bush, produces four different essential oils – one with a wintergreen odor from the bark, the second with an allspice odor from the berries, the third with a camphor odor from the twigs, and the fourth with a lavender odor from the leaves.

In many cases all the species in a genus have the same scent type. The large Composite family that includes the asters, Rudbeckias, mums, and sunflowers includes few scented species, probably because they are bee-pollinated and do not need them.

The word perfume comes from the Latin *per* and *fumare* and means to perfuse with smoke, an apparent reference to the religious custom dating from ancient times of making burnt offerings of scented woods and incense.

Perfumers have some 4000 raw materials to work with, most of them plant products. Some scents blend nicely, others clash. A perfume has a top note that gives an initial surprise reaction, a middle note that is the true lasting scent, and a bottom note that is the last thing you perceive as the odor fades. Perfumers depend heavily on the flowers of roses, hyacinths, and acacias and the foliage of lavender, geranium, and rosemary.

There are four common commercial methods of extracting essential oils from plants. Because they are not damaged by the heating, the attars of roses and of orange blossoms are made by *distillation*, a process most often used to obtain the oils from leaves, barks, and wood. Steam is forced through the petals in a closed container and it cooks the essential oil from the tissue. When the steam is cooled the oil floats on top of the water and can easily be removed in pure form.

Types that will not withstand heating are often removed by *solvent extraction* in which petroleum ether soaks through the petals and dissolves the oil which is then recovered by separating it from the ether. This process gives the purest form of the essential oil, called the "floral absolute".

Enfleurage is expensive because it requires much hand labor but it preserves some of the subtle scents that will not survive the harsher treatments. Fresh flowers like those of the jasmines are layered between screens coated with animal fat so that the plant oils will go into solution in the animal fat as they evaporate from the petals since lipids dissolve in lipids. Later alcohol is used to remove the essential oil from the fat.

Expression is used mostly to obtain citrus oils. The citrus peel is crushed and the oil washed from the debris. The oil is then separated from the wash water.

Chapter 20

These are Rose's "Behaviors"

An area where many will draw a strong distinction between plants and animals is the life characteristic often listed as *irritability*, the capacity to respond fairly directly to some stimulus. Much of what we find so fascinating about animals is there complicated repertoires of behaviors but in this respect plants are disappointing since most of their responses to external stimuli are slow and easily overlooked. Compared to a cheetah chasing a Thompson's gazelle that can turn faster and keep going longer a tree abscissing a leaf burdened with epiphytic algae won't win any awards for excitement.

Complicated behaviors that involve a series of responses with some interaction between two individuals, like the mating ceremonies of many birds, are quite beyond the plants. Both the physical limitations imposed on movement by cell walls and the routine use of animals or physical forces as intermediaries for pollination suggests that the needs of the plants are simpler and their kinds and variety of responses are too.

Dandelions making flowers on tall stems in unmowed areas but only on short stems that are below the rotary blade level where the turf is mowed regularly is undeniably an adaptation to local conditions. Similarly a branch broken from a willow that makes adventitious roots and becomes a new tree some distance away is an adaptative response. And a bush or tree changing from sun leaves with a double layer of palisade cells to shade leaves with only a single layer as competitors begin to overtop it is adaptive. However although these others responses are important none of these is considered a behavior in the sense this chapter is considering because none involves the movement of body parts.

The kinds of responses that we loosely call plant behaviors are those movements that we define as either tropisms or nastic movements. In both categories the mechanical cause of the movement may be either differences in the growth rates on two sides of an organ, or differential changes in cell turgor within areas of the organ.

Growth movements are hard to reverse. They result from differential growth by faster cell division and elongation on one side of a petiole, petal, or other organ than the other. For instance, young leaves, bud scales, and petals initially grow faster on the lower than the upper sides so that they curve in and protect the center of the organ. Later they grow faster on the upper than the lower surfaces and curve out, opening the bud, flower, etc.

Turgor movements are readily reversed. They result from differential changes in the turgor or water pressure within certain cells and consequently their size. The rolling of many grass leaves in dry weather, which is an obvious mechanism to reduce water loss by reducing the amount of exposed surface, in such a movement. The action is premeditated since the smooth curving in the right direction depends on longitudinal rows of large, thin-walled bulliform cells on one leaf surface or the other. These change size most substantially as they lose turgor and thus assure that their surface if the inside of the curve.

In some flowers the stamens give a very fast movement in response to touch that literally slaps them against the object, which is usually an insect, protruding into the blossom. While being treated this way must annoy the bees it does them no harm and it guarantees that they are well dusted with pollen.

One of the most fascinating because very easily observed examples of a rapid movement in a plant is the folding of the compound leaves of *Mimosa pudica*, the so called "sensitive plant", when they are touched. This is also a turgor movement. Large pulvini cells at the base of the leaflets lose turgor rapidly to produce the leaf collapse response. The unresolved questions concern how the stimulus is transmitted through the plant so that other leaves also collapse even if only one is touched. The speed of transmission makes it unlikely that a hormone can be the cause and there have been studies trying to determine if some electric phenomenon analogous to what happens in nerve transmissions is involved as some have suggested.

Tropisms are paratonic movements, those made in response to and oriented in relation to some external stimulus coming from a particular direction. The movements may be positive (movement toward the stimulus), negative (movement away from the stimulus), or lateral (movement perpendicular to the stimulus, like a stem growing across the soil rather than upright). These movements are phototropism, gravitropism, chemotropism, and haptotropism.

Observing plants, especially trees, growing on a steep hill it is obvious that the stems grow straight up, not straight out. But, the stems will try to right themselves if pushed over at an angle. So the plants must have some way of detecting gravity.

In 1709 Austroc described the effect of gravity on the vertical shoot-root orientation of plants. John Hunter who died in 1793 seems to have been the first to experiment with the effect of rotation as a counteracting force to gravity on plant orientation but in 1806 T.A. Knight set up the demonstration that made European scientists take note. He devised a water powered device that rotated an eleven inch diameter disk at 150 r.p.m. and grew plants on this whirling dervish of a device. They responded by aiming their shoots toward the center of the disk and growing their roots straight out toward the periphery. In the 1870s the phenomenon was named geotropism. In the 1970s the name gravitropism was introduced as a more precise term to replace that and I will use it here.

In his book *Plantwatching* (Facts On File Pub., 1988) Malcolm Wilkins compared the task of getting the emerging root of a seed deep into the soil so that it can provide anchorage as well as water absorption to sending a space capsule on a mission. Both need guidance systems which he defines as mechanisms designed to ensure that a body moving through space keeps to a pre-arranged course. Such a system needs three elements: a sensing mechanism to detect any deviation from the pre-set course, a response mechanism to restore it to the correct course if it does deviate, and some mechanism to connect those two components since they are often located a distance apart.

In gravitropism the initial root of the seedling responds to an uneven distribution of hormones and curves so it grows as close to straight down as it can manage. The stimulus is gravity, the connector is a hormone unequally distributed, and the adaptative response is differential growth that produces curvature of the organ. But how do plants detect gravity? They use a mechanism well developed in many animals – particles heavy enough that they are always pulled by gravity toward the lowest part of the structure where they cause a stimulation. The hormone itself cannot be the detector because it is in solution and individual molecules are too small to be significantly affected by gravity. In our inner ears such particles, actually pieces of calcium carbonate or marble, press into a jelly-like matrix and stimulate nerve endings. Based on our experience, our brains interpret where our bodies are in space based on which nerves are being stimulated. In plants somewhat similar structures exist but they are within individual cells called statocytes and instead of two inner ear units for the whole body each root tip and shoot has some.

The structures inside the cells in place of pieces of marbles are called amyloplasts or "starch-containing bodies" because each is a membrane-wrapped packets of clumps of starch. They sink to the lowest side of the cell if the plant is laid on its side. Probably this movement affects the cell membrane, maybe because of the electric change found on the amyloplasts. Somehow it brings about the uneven distribution of a hormone and the subsequent differential growth but those details are still being studied. In the root amyloplasts are found only in the root cap cells. In stems they are scattered along the stems, usually in rings around the vascular bundle.

How can we be sure the amyloplasts are the gravity detection mechanism? First, all of the organs that respond to gravity have them. Second, the packets move to the lower side of cells if the plant is laid on its side and they do so faster than the plant gives any sign that it has detected its tilt, a necessary condition if the packets are really involved in the detection process. And third, if they are removed the organ loses its ability to tell the direction. If they are chemically removed the root grows randomly but if they are allowed to reform the orientation ability returns with them. Pretty good evidence.

The best indication that gravitropism is genetically controlled is the discovery several years ago of a strain of peas that lacks the response. They should tell us a lot about the process precisely because of what they cannot do and the structures they do not have when compared with responsive strains of the same species.

In stems the gravitropism response is due to a shift in the levels of auxin and gibberellins at the upper and lower sides of the stem leading to accelerated growth of the lower surface. In roots there often is no evidence of auxin in the root cap. Here there is evidence that abscisic acid (ABA) is involved and that it is inhibition of the growth of the lower surface rather than stimulation of faster growth of the upper surface that curves the root and aims it deeper into the soil. Different specifics but the same result.

There are three general categories of plant growth responses to light: photomorphogenesis, photoperiodism, and phototropism.

Photomorphogenesis refers to responses that depend on light stimulation that does not need to be either directional or periodic. Seed germination, stem elongation, leaf unrolling, and other structural and functional features occur only when there is light to signal the season is right or the investment in the growth will payoff in more photosynthesis. One of the decisions that had to be made during the evolution of the plants outside the tropics was whether to recognize the seasons by the temperature or the daylength. Those types that went with daylength are with us today to show their stuff, the others succumbed to the occasional severe early or late frosts long ago. By allowing gradual and highly predictable daylength rather than notably undependable weather generalities to call the shots the plants can anticipate the onset of unsuitable conditions and go into dormancy in time to salvage some of the valuable chemicals in the body parts that will be abscissed and have time to convert to the metabolic systems that will remain functional when things get cold and/or dry. In the spring the lilacs and the tulips will come up at about the same time every year because a few warm days in February won't trick them into bursting into bloom then.

As we saw in **Chapter 18**, photoperiodism refers to responses that depend on the detection of changes in the alternating daily light and darkness pattern to time activities like flowering.

Phototropism is the short-term growth response to a directional light stimulus. It is short term because it only influences the growth as long as the light is coming from a particular direction. If later in the season the competition moves in and the light reaching the plant is coming from another direction the phototropic response will shift those parts able to respond to take best advantage of the light now reaching it from another angle. If the plant receives good light from all around it will grow upright with little indication that it is responding to the light at all since the zig is balancing the zag.

The Roman scholar Varro described the curvature of some flower stems toward the light about 100 A.D. It was Charles Darwin and his son Francis who helped bring the subject back to the attention of educated people with their 1881 book describing a long series of experimental studies on the effect of light on the growing tip of oat seedlings. The Darwins established that the shoot's light sensing mechanism was located in the tip even though the growth response occurred several millimeters away.

About thirty years later P. Boysen-Jensen in Denmark continued the work and showed that whatever factor was moving from the tip could pass through a piece of gelatin inserted between it and the rest of the shoot and produce the normal effect. In 1918 Arpad Paal in Hungary showed that if the tip was cut off and replaced so that it was off-center the shoot bent even when it was not exposed to light so he argued that the uneven distribution of some chemical caused the bending. In 1928 Fritz Went in Holland proved Paal right by showing that the chemical could be captured in blocks of agar placed under the severed tips and that the angle of bending depended on how much of the chemical reached each side of the shoot. His work led directly to the isolation of the chemical which we now know as Indoleacetic acid (IAA) or auxin. As a sign of the quirkiness of science, the first auxin to be chemically identified was not isolated from plants but from human urine.

In the 1920s N.J. Cholodny and F. Went proposed that the growth effect resulted from the uneven distribution of the growth substance that was transported laterally across the petiole or other organ in response to the stimulus. It took the work of W.R. Briggs and his colleagues in the 1950s to finally resolve some of the questions about this and convince everyone that the auxin produced in the shoot tip *is* laterally transported to the shaded side where, since it is a growth stimulant, it makes the cells on that side growth faster and that results in a curvature of the petiole or stem. How it moves in response to the light is still being worked out. After extensive research it now seems that the light detector involved in the phototropism response is the yellow pigment riboflavin.

Skototropism is essentially reverse phototropism. It occurs in some vines like *Monstera* as they grow toward the dark spots around them seeking a treetrunk to climb. For such a vine growing into the bright spot will guarantee never finding anything large to climb up. Similarly ivy (*Hedera*) vines also grow away from the light until they find a vertical surface to climb and adhesive roots only form on their shaded side. Once the plant finds a suitable object to climb it becomes positively phototropic.

Haptotropism, a directed response to touch, is seen in various petioles (eg. *Clematis*), leaf tips (eg. *Gloriosa*, the climbing lily), and aerial roots (eg. *Vanilla* orchid) that will curve toward the touched side if slightly rubbed with a stick. Tendrils are especially sensitive.

Chemotropism is a reaction to certain gases and water soluble chemicals. We see it most clearly when a pollen tube curves to follow a sugar concentration gradient on a lab dish or within a flower.

These tropism mechanisms are not absolute and they vary depending on the needs of the plant. The initial root and shoot show a strong response to gravity but their branches have weaker reactions – otherwise all roots would grow straight down instead of spreading out laterally, and every tree would have only a tight bundle of almost vertical branches instead of a spreading crown. Bermuda grass and some other sprawling species may grow more upright in poor light (where they are probably competing with nearby plants) than in strong light, so they are positively phototropic in dim light but negatively so in bright light.

Nastic movements or nasties (and you thought botanists had no sense of humor) are those that depend on some stimulus but are independent of its direction. These moves are determined and limited by the existing structures of the organ and typically act in hinge-like fashion. These include thermonasty, photonasty, haptonasty, chemonasty, seismonasty, and stomate movements.

Thermonasty is a response to a change in temperature. For instance, as a result of differential growth on the two sides of the petals crocus or tulip flowers open when it warms up and close when it cools down again.

Photonasty is a response to a change in light intensity, as in the darkness triggered "sleep" folding of the leaves of some species and when the flowers of *Portulaca* open in the sun but close again if they are shaded.

Haptonasy, a response to touch, and chemonasty, a response to specific molecule types, are seen mostly in the insectivorous plants where the movement or the presence of certain chemicals that is the equivalent of a taste may indicate prey.

Seismonasty refers to large and rapid touch responses like the leaf collapse movements of *Mimosa pudica* and the moves of some stamens to dust visiting insects with pollen.

Autonomic movements are those that need no stimulus, they are self-starting as it were. These include the circumnutation of a vine seeking an object to cling to and the twining growth of various tendrils and leaves.

Depending on the species, the nyctinastic or leaf-folding "sleep" movements may be in response to a loss of light or a consequent drop in temperature. In *Oxalis* the onset of darkness results in the closing of the leaves by turgor movements and the closing of the flowers by growth movements.

Hygroscopic movements usually occur in dead cells and result from either water uptake or the drying of the cells, or repeated shifts from one condition to the other. Some grass seeds with awns or "tails" literally screw themselves into the soil and plant themselves as the long tails coil and uncoil with changes in the humidity.

Cohesion movements are those that result from the water uptake by dead cells (only rarely live ones) and cause a curvature in a structure. This is what opens anthers to release the pollen and opens the spore cases or sporangia of various ferns and other lower plant types to release the spores.

Circadian ("around a day") rhythms are daily patterns of physiological responses, including some movements, that are genetically programmed into an organism. They are well studied in many animals and ourselves and there is some evidence of them in plants. As early as 1729 Jean-Jacques de Mairan pointed out that some of the regular movements of the leaves of some plant that raise and lower them daily continue for several days even in dim light. The trick to detecting an inborn rhythmic behavior among the movements that are strict responses to light or other environmental cues is to keep the plants under constant conditions and see if the rhythm continues. Today we know that in plants these behaviors run down and stop after several days without the environmental stimuli. The fact that they continue for those few days is the critical point though since it means there is something more than just a response to environmental cues involved. Under lab conditions the biological clock that such a rhythmic pattern seems to require can be reset and made to run faster or slower. The still unresolved problem is exactly what the clock is. In many but not all species there is clear evidence that phytochrome is involved but what cellular chemistry does it turn on and off and how?

CHAPTER 21

THIS IS ROSE'S TAXONOMIC CLASSIFICATION

Have you ever heard anyone ask someone who works with plants professionally, "Why can't you just use simple names for the plants instead of the fancy Latin ones that don't mean anything and are only a way of showing off?" Have you ever been tempted to ask the question yourself? I am going to try to answer the question for you here.

Do you realize that if you bought a "plush rose", a "rose of sharon," and a "rose moss" you would not have a single member of the *Rose* family in the group? Would you be surprised and/or disappointed if you ordered plants of "Glory bower" and "Bleeding heart vine" by mail and you got received two identical plants? What about a "Spider plant"? Is it *Cleome spinosa*, an annual Dicot garden flower that grows four feet high and has large masses of purple, pink, or white flowers with a new group opening every day held above the foliage or *Chlorophytum elatum*, a hanging basket Monocot houseplant with narrow leaves and little plants that form on the long runners after the inconspicuous white flowers have faded? And is it different from an "Airplane plant".

These examples illustrate the problem of having not only everyone in a local area but everyone in the world talk about a species of plant and know they are all talking about exactly the same kind of plant. This is what makes the use of "technical" names essential and more people are taking them in stride every day.

Proper taxonomic names involve more than showing off, they mean accuracy when and where it counts. It may serve your own purposes to talk about your "Mexican rose" but if you want to purchase one by mail from a distance or even correspond with plant lovers in other parts of the country about your plant you had better be more exact in your naming than that or you may cause everyone a lot of confusion. What you want to discuss or order is *Dombeya cayeuxii* everywhere. It may have a dozen different common names but they will not cause confusion if you also specify the taxonomic name. Typical of the problems with common names is the marsh marigold (*Caltha palustris*) which has more than 80 different local names in Britain, some 60 more in France, and at least 140 others in Germany, Austria and Switzerland.

And the problem works both ways. Several different species may have the same common name, and the same species may have several different common names. Thus seven different *Salix* species are called "Black willow" and *Gleditsia triacanthos* is known as Honey Locust and at least thirteen other common names.

The technical name of a species gives those familiar with the basics of the classification system a great deal of information. Just the names themselves, for instance, tell you which types are closely and which are only more distantly related. Thus "Damask rose" (*Rosa damascena*), "Chinese rose" (*Rosa chinensis*) and "French rose" (*Rosa gallica*) are closely related but "baby sun rose" (*Aptenia cordifolia*), "copper rose" (*Echeveria multicaulis,* "cotton rose" (*Hibiscus mutabilis*), "desert rose" (*Adenium obesum*), "Rose of china" (*Hibiscus rosa-sinensis*), "Christmas rose" (*Helleborus niger*) and "rose heath" (*Erica gracilis*) are all "roses" in an extended sense only. They are not closely related botanically to the garden roses and none of them is as closely related to any of the others as the French, Chinese, and Damask roses are.

It must be conceded that the taxonomic classification system is less than perfect because new proposals are being made for classification schemes regularly and occasionally a species has a "new" name and an "old" name simultaneously because a new scheme has been proposed and generally accepted for the plant group but the scheme is still unofficial. Thus *Philodendron oxycardium*, the philodendron most commonly grown as a houseplant, is also knows as *Philodendron cordatum* and *Philodendron scandens* in different classification systems. A procedural note. It is common practice when writing taxonomic names that if the same genus name, the first one of the two part name, is used for two or more species mentioned in sequence the genus name may be abbreviated in the second and following references. Thus it would have been appropriate to list *P. cordatum* and *P. scandens* here.

In the case of the "Heartleaf" philodendron above, it is the species name that is in dispute. In some cases both the genus and species names may be different in proposed classification schemes for a particular group. Thus "Devil's ivy" or Pothos can be found classified as *Scindapsus aureaus, Pothos aureus, Raphidophora aureus* and *Epipremnum aureus* by different authorities. The classification of any species is by no means final and absolute.

Even common food plants have different common names as you travel about. What is corn (*Zea mays*) in the U.S. is maize in Britain where corn means wheat or some other small grain. What you probably call summer squash is vegetable marrow in Britain and courgettes in much of Europe. Your eggplant is an aubergine elsewhere.

A common objection is that the Latin names are too difficult to pronounce yet we do so without complaint for many species that have never received common names. Species like *Aster, Azalea, Chrysanthemum, Hydrangea, Iris, Nasturtium, Petunia* and *Sequoia* use the Latin name directly. Many other plant names in English are only slight modifications of the Latin word. Consider *pinus, lilium, viola, orchis, cedrus,* and *rosa*. Note that Latin is used for all the names because, being a dead language the words do not change their meaning with time, and because the change of endings allows the same root word to be used at several levels of the classification system without actual duplication.

The second most common objection is that the names don't mean anything. It could be argued that "Pussy ears" (*Cyanotis somaliensis*) or "Teddy bear plant" (*Cyanotis kewensis*) are hardly meaningful but it is more productive to emphasize that many of the species names are descriptive terms and tell you something about the plant just by knowing its name. Consider: *acaulis* (stemless); *arborescence* (woody); *caerulus* (dark blue); *cardifolius* (heart-shaped leaves); *dentatus* (toothed); *discolor* (of two colors).

A specific name makes sense because it is the only way to deal with the differences. You don't deal with a "mailman", it is Mr. So-and-so. You don't go into a garage and just order tires to install yourself, you order a specific size, type and brand. If you order just "a begonia" from a grower you might get any of more than 1200 species and thousands of hybrids and cultivars. That is comparable to calling a bookstore and ordering a novel without giving any further specifications. You may get pretty near anything – and probably the most expensive one of its type.

Knowing the proper taxonomic names of the plant species is also essential in many cases if you want to look up how to care for them in the different garden or houseplant books. The only way for an author to get around the problem of the same plant being called half a dozen different names in different parts of the country is to refer to it by its taxonomic name. And it is really no more difficult to call a plant *Episcia* than it is "flame violet", or *Abutilon* rather than "flowering maple". This will also eliminate the confusion which results from common names that suggest that plants are related when they are not.

Becoming acquainted with the classification system also makes us more aware of the close relationship between some plants that you might not have realized were "kissin' cousins". Broccoli (*Brassica oleracea italica*), cabbage (*Brassica oleracea capitata*), turnips (*Brassica rapa*), and radishes (*Raphanus sativus*), for instance, are all members of the mustard family (*Cruciferae* or *Brassicaceae*). Although they may at first seem very dissimilar, if you examine their flowers you find exactly the same pattern in each case – 4 sepals, 4 separate petals, 6 stamens (2 short and 4 long) and one pistil. It is features like these that are used to group species in the taxonomical system.

It helps to know where these taxonomic names come from and what they represent. At present there are about 300,000 kinds of plants identified, each with a unique combination of structural features, growth pattern, method of reproduction, and other characteristics. Biologists have attempted to come up with a single classification system that would include all of those plus more than a million known kinds of animals. That means that we need a system that will sort any living thing into the right bin out of more than 1.4 million cubbyholes. There is such a system. The one that gives us those fancy names for species. The interesting thing about the name that we give to a kind of plant or animal is that it is really a shorthand designation. In two words it gives us a wealth of information including at least five other names which are simply understood when the two are given.

We start the classification of all living things by sorting them into groups that have certain structural or chemical features in common and which differ from those of all the other groups. To have the system work it is very important that the groups are always non-overlapping. At each level of the system there is one and only one of the subgroups into which each and every type of living thing will fit based on its characteristics. We call these first large groups the *Kingdoms*. In the original and simplest scheme only two kingdoms were designated, Plant and Animal. Today the system most used recognizes five kingdoms (Bacteria, Fungi, single celled Protists, Plants, and Animals).

Next we take each kingdom and further subdivide its members into two or more non-overlapping groups called *Divisions* for plants and *Phyla* for animals. Sometimes *Subdivisions* are designated also. Here again the critical feature is that all the members of a particular Division have certain structural or physiological features in common and those features are not found in the members of any other Division.

Each Division can then be subdivided in a similar manner on the basis of similarities and differences into two or more *Classes* (and sometimes *subclasses*) and they in turn can be subdivided into *Orders*, which can be subdivided into *Families* (which may be divided into *subfamilies* and/or *tribes*). Beyond the Family level the organisms, now separated out into relatively small groups with quite similar features, can divided into *Genera* (singular = Genus), and finally into *species* the last subgroups in the simplest classification scheme.

So the descending group titles (in the simplest scheme) are:

Kingdom
    Division
        Class
            Order
                Family
                    Genus
                        species.

This, the universally agreed upon basic scheme, is a hierarchical system. Every species is part of one and only one genus; each genus is part of one and only one family; and so on up the line. No other lifeform alive or extinct is given that species name in combination with that genus name.

Each step in this system divides all of the organisms in the large group of the step above into two or more non-overlapping subgroups so it is a dichotomous or two-division scheme. The printed description of the characteristics and the assigned taxonomic names is called a *key*.

This system is similar to an address system with each species having a unique address and with that address giving considerable information about the kind of creature involved. When you address a letter to a friend at a particular house number on a certain street in a certain town in a certain state you supply five pieces of information (name, house number, street, city, state) from which several others are automatically understood because the people operating the postal system know basic geography. For instance, if the address is in Pennsylvania we know, and therefore need not specify, that it is in the U.S.A., in North America and on the planet earth.

In the address system you need five separate pieces of information on the envelope to assure it reaching the right person because the naming system for streets and cities permits the same name to be used in more than one place. Thus almost every city has a Market street and there are Philadelphias in several states, etc. The taxonomic system abbreviates the address system by forbidding the use of exactly the same name in any two different places in the system except the species level, the very last essential division level. Therefore we only need two names in the taxonomic system to uniquely specify each type of living thing. In this system when you specify the two names, the genus and the species, you tell anyone familiar with the classification system what family, order, class, division, and kingdom the living thing is in. And since each of those groups is characterized by a specific set of structural and functional features this informed person immediately knows a lot about the needs and potentials of the new plant because he or she knows it has the combination of all those traits. That is a lot of useful information from a simple two word name.

Originally all of the sorting out in the classification system was done on the basis of similarities and differences in the structures of the plant body parts and their reproductive processes. Today biochemical differences are also being considered as part of the system.

In the flowering plants the flower and fruit structures are major criteria for classification And this for very good reason. The reproduction parts of the plant – flower, seed and fruit are those least affected and altered by environmental factors. A *Rosa canina* plant that we can grow and get to flower virtually anywhere will have the same number and arrangement of the flower parts no matter what the size of the flower or the shape of the rest of the plant.

If we took seeds from the same garden flower and grew half of them in full sun and half in partial shade or other contrasting conditions the resulting plants might be very different in size, number, and shape of leaves, the color of the shoot parts, the length of the stems, the extent of root growth, etc. since these are all easily and drastically affected by environmental factors like the amount of sunlight, soil nutrients, and moisture. But if the plants from both growing areas succeeded in flowering and setting seeds and we grew all of those seeds under the same conditions the next year – either all in full sun or all in shade – we probably could not tell from looking at them which ones had come from which group of parent plants. And while there might be differences in the number and size of the flowers produced by the groups of plants in the different growing areas, the number and arrangement of the flower parts would be exactly the same.

The taxonomic or classification system that is used today is presumed to show the evolutionary relationships among the various types of organisms. Those that have common ancestors in fairly recent times will show a lot of similarities in body parts. Those that are only more distantly related (i.e., it has been longer since they had common ancestors) will have fewer similarities. This presumption of close common ancestry, for which there is a great deal of scientific evidence, often indicates that species of widely different evolutionary lines have all adapted to a specific set of environmental conditions in very similar ways. Taking a look at the vegetative plant parts can very deceiving about the ancestry of the species. Some members of the Cactus family (*Cactaceae*), the Milkweed family (*Asclepiadaceae*), and the Spurge family (*Euphorbiaceae*) have all evolved very similar barrel-shaped stems, spines, thick waterproofing cutin layer and other adaptive features for surviving in deserts. They appear very similar. But examining their flowers it is immediately obvious that they are members of quite different groups of plants. If you are a succulent fancier, for instance, and you are trying to get interesting new plants by cross pollinating among your collection, you have virtually no chance of getting seed to form unless the plants are both members of at least the same family and often only between those of the same genus.

Rose's full taxonomic description is:

Kingdom	-	Plant
Division	-	Spermatophytes
Subdivision	-	Angiosperms
Class	-	Dicotyledons
Subclass	-	Rosidae
Order	-	Rosales

Family   - Rosaceae
Genus   - Rosa
Species   - canina

Taxonomic descriptions written for those "in the business" use many technical terms to be as succinct as possible. To illustrate I will reprint here the descriptions of the family, tribe, genus, and species of Rose from one of the standards, the revised seventh edition of Asa Gray's *New Manual of Botany* (American Book Co.), published in 1908.

Rosaceae = Rose family: Plants with regular flowers, numerous (rarely few) distinct stamens inserted on the calyx, and one to many pistils, which are quite distinct (or in the second tribe) united and combined with the calyx-tube. Ovules (anatropous) one to few in each ovary; seeds almost always without albumen. Embryo straight, with large and thick cotyledons. Leaves alternate, with stipules. Calyx of 5 (3-8) sepals (the odd one superior), united at the base, often appearing double by a row of bractlets outside. Petals as many as sepals (rarely wanting), mostly imbricated in the bud, and inserted with the stamens on the edge of a disk that lines the calyx-tube. Trees, shrubs, or herbs.

Tribe VI - *Roseae*: Pistils many, becoming bony achenes, enclosed in the globose or urn-shaped fleshy calyx-tube, which resembles a pome. Petals conspicuous. Stamens numerous.

Genus 23 - *Rosa*: Calyx-tube, urn-shaped, contracted at the mouth, becoming fleshy in the fruit. Petals five, obovate or obsordate, inserted with the many stamens into the edge of the hollow thin disk that lines the calyx-tube and within bears the numerous pistils below. Ovaries hairy, becoming bony achenes in fruit. Shrubs, usually prickly, with odd-pinnate leaves, and stipules adnate to the petiole; stalks, foliage, etc. often bearing aromatic glands. Many of the species highly variable and often indeterminable from imperfect specimens (The ancient Latin name.)

An excerpt of the relevant parts of his key to the species looks like this for two of the fifteen species he lists as found in the Central and Northeastern United States and adjacent Canada.

    a=styles distinct
        b=sepals connivent after flowering, persistent; pedicels and receptacle naked
        - prickles not uniform

- outer calyx-lobes conspicuously pinnatifid =
   Rosa canina

bb=sepals spreading after flowering, deciduous from the mature fruit; receptacle and pedicels more or less hispid or tomentose
   - leaflets membranaceous; receptacle not tomentose
   - leaf rhachis puberulent or glabrous; scarcely if at all glandular
   - Young growth armed at node if at all
      - stipules dilated, oblanceolate; infrastipular prickles longer than 6 mm.
      - Prickles decidedly curved; leaflets somewhat shining above
            = *Rosa virginiana*

Then his detailed descriptions of those two species.

Rosa canina (Dog rose): Stems armed with stout recurved prickles, the branches somewhat unarmed; leaflets 5-7, elliptical or oblong-ovate, glabrous or somewhat pubescent, simply toothed, non-resinous-puberulent; flowers solitary (or 2-4) on usually naked pedicels; sepals pinnatifid; fruit ovoid or nearly globular. A casual escape from cultivation Mass. to Tenn.; thoroughly naturalized on river banks in Pa. Introduced from Eurasia.

Rosa virginiana: stems often tall and stout (2-20 decimeters high) with at length stout and usually more or less hooked prickles; stipules usually naked, more or less dilated; leaflets (mostly 7) dark green, rather thick, smooth and often shining above; flowers corymbose or solitary; outer sepals frequently with 1 or 2 small lobes. Margins of swamps and rocky shores, New Foundland to Florida, west to Minnesota, Missouri, Okhlahoma and Louisiana.

CHAPTER 22

THESE ARE ROSE'S LIFE CYCLES, DORMANCY AND SENESCENCE

All organisms must get energy to power the chemical and physical processes essential to life, must obtain components they need to build and repair their structures, and must deal with stresses resulting from environmental conditions. Plants derive all of their energy and building materials from the inorganic or non-living environment and we can understand many aspects of their life cycles as adaptations to an *autotrophic* or "self-feeding" existence. Because they depend on photosynthesis they need to efficiently expose tissues to light and because they need to take in minerals from the soil they develop roots which take care of the water supply problem at the same time.

The life cycle of a flowering plant like Rose includes several discrete stages that occur in sequence. Life begins with the fertilization that leads to its formation in the form of a seed. Its first activity is to develop from a single cell to a small multicellular embryo which will then go into dormancy to await the environmental conditions that will stimulate it back to active growth at germination. In the seed the embryo carries on a minimum of essential biochemical life functions, utilizing the food stores packaged into it by the parent plant for its energy source. Through the weeks and months of dormancy the young plant is largely unresponsive but protected by its inactivity from much of the potential harm of temperature extremes, dryness, and poor light conditions that would threaten an actively growing plant.

With the coming of good growing conditions, whether that is spring or the rainy season, the embryonic plant stirs to life and beings a frantic period of rapid growth. It must develop enough primary root, leaf, and stem to permit it to absorb nutrients and water and position its photosynthetic tissue in the light before it exhausts its supply of stored food. The young plant adds secondary growth as it matures vegetatively. The mature plant produces flowers. The flowers are pollinated and a new generation of seeds develop within them. And the cycle repeats. For a perennial species like Rose the picture gets a bit more complicated because the mature plant intersplices senescence, abscission, and dormancy with repeats of the mature stage events so that the plant may coexist with its offspring of many different years, each of which is going through its own repeats of the whole process.

The major problem for the young plant shifts but remains somewhat the same. It must find and maintain its place in the sun, a bit of growing area with sufficient light exposure to meet its needs, and its share of the water and soil minerals. As a seed the initial problem was to get its shoot out of the soil and into the light; as a seedling it has to compete with all of the other plants in its immediate area, both the established ones and the other new seedlings, to maintain its position and share of the resources.

Which of several competitive strategies this plant will utilize has largely been predetermine by its genes which have the coded instructions accumulated by the species over long periods of evolutionary time. It may concentrate on growing taller than the competition so as to shade them out and avoid being shaded out itself as canopy layer trees do. It may have metabolic adaptations that permit it to survive and even thrive on less light or other resources than the competition as understory layer trees and shrubs do. Or it may develop a timing mechanism that will permit it to grow quickly and complete most of its essential activities in a short period of the year when the competitors are still dormant and leafless and then go dormant itself and avoid their shade as many spring bulbs do.

As it succeeds in storing more energy-rich organic molecules than it needs to burn up in the short run for its energy needs the plant can convert those molecules into the components of additional cells and can grow and develop into a mature specimen.

Quiescence is when a plant is not actively growing because some basic condition is absent (e.g., it lacks sufficient nutrients) but it will resume normal activity as soon as that deficiency ends. Some seeds will sprout as soon as wetted and therefore are not truly dormant. Dormancy is a state of suspended activity usually requiring careful preparations and specific initiating conditions. Breaking out of it also usually requires special conditions that are often different from a simple reversal of the ones that initiated it. In true dormancy the plant is usually tolerant to cold, water loss, and other adverse conditions.

Studies have found that among the plants there are many different ways of getting dead. From a physiological point of view many manifestations of senescence are aspects of development carried out in an orderly fashion and they are adaptive for the plant as a whole in many ways. There are clear implications that senescence leads to programmed death since it is not a chaotic breakdown but shows pattern and sequence. It is an orderly retreat, especially when the productive capacity and the resources of the plant have been rechanneled into seed production. Loss of chlorophyll and proteins are key changes in senescence but the process is a complex of many parallel and sequential steps, some not all of them reversible. Senescence of the whole plant is tied to some internal development program, not the clock or the calendar. And there are many variations in the specifics, the timing, and the sequences of events between species so we do not expect that the initiating signals or the intermediate stages of the senescence progression will be the same in all cases.

A.C. Leopold suggests in his contribution to *Senescence in Plants* (CRC Press, 1980) that life is like a candle flame that has persistent characteristics even though its constituent parts are continuously being exhausted and renewed and that an organism is similarly a population of cells, tissues, organelles, and substrate that are constantly being exhausted and renewed. He then notes that the simile extends to the biosphere which exists because of a continuously exhausted and renewed supply of organisms. Aging and senescence assure the ready turnover of materials and facilitate the continuous renewal.

In 1952 P.B. Medawar who received the Nobel Prize in 1960 for his work in immunology described senescence as deteriorative changes which lead sooner or later to the natural death of the organism or some part of it. He distinguished this from aging that is the processes of accruing maturity that occur in time without reference to death as a consequence. Botanists generally talk about senescence in plants but zoologists tend to talk about aging, perhaps because senescence without the death of the whole organism is common in plants but much less so in animals. In plants senescence can be mapped out in changes in cells, tissues, and organs at each successive stage of the life of the organism.

The biosphere is dynamic and so are all its constituents so turnover is essential both to get around the problems of shortage of resources and to allow the evolutionary process since it takes new generations with new combinations of genes to adapt to changing environments. Rapid turnover with a large number of offspring can be an advantage in the evolutionary race under rapidly changing environmental conditions.

A study compared two species of *Mimulus* or Monkey flower that grow widely in the Rocky mountain states. *M. cardinalis* with red flowers and eighty times more nectar per flower is pollinated by hummingbirds while the nearby *M. lewisii* with pink flowers and little nectar depends on bumblebees. The researchers found that much of the difference in the traits of flower color and amount of nectar produced was controlled by only a small number of "master genes" that each have a larger than average impact among the group of genes totally responsible for each trait. This means it would require fewer changes than previously thought to start two groups down the genetic pathway to becoming separate species.

The half life of a molecule type or organelle is the time before half of those units within the cell will have been destroyed or become non-functional in some way. We do not know a lot about the half lives of most molecule types because it simply is not a matter of high research priority but we have enough numbers to give us some idea of the ranges. In animal liver cells peroxisomes have a half life of one to two days and ribosomal RNA molecules about five days. Animal liver cell mitochondria have a half life of five to six days which means that some measurements that found another mitochondrion starting to be removed by autophagy every ten minutes should be about right. The bottom line is that everything within living things from individual molecules on up wears out and must be replaced piece by piece on a regular basis. The turnover of individual molecules and organelles seems fairly random while cell types have more predictable life expectancies. Making homeostatic adjustments by adding or deleting molecules or organelles is easy, getting rid of cells and organs is possible but takes more time and work.

The generalization holds that the average survival of biological systems increases with complexity. Cells survive longer than their organelles, an organism survives longer than its cells, and a species survives longer than any of its members.

Whole populations of soybeans, corn, etc. die simultaneously soon after seedset and usually well before winter conditions arrive but, with only a few exceptions like salmon, animals seldom die *en masse* naturally after a single breeding event. Other plant species routinely survive their first winter but die the second year after they have set seed. Some, like *Viola tricolor*, that normally flower and die in one year will overwinter in a vegetative state with little difficulty if prevented from making flowers the first year.

Some of the aging decline in woody plants seems to result from the increasing limitations of physiological activity in the older and larger mass of stems and not due to loss of totipotency of the individual cells. The fact that pruning routinely rejuvenates many species seems to confirm this analysis.

Animals are more tightly integrated than plants. A plant can be senescent and still yield cuttings that grow vigorously into healthy new individuals but nothing comparable happens in animals. Also changes in one animal organ or system affect all the others to a greater degree than happens in plants.

The genomes of animals seem to suffer more damage (or become less efficient at DNA repair) with age resulting in the formation of more cancers and other tumors in older individuals and more congenital defects in the offspring of older mothers, but plants generally hold up better. There are clones of vegetatively propagated crop types that have been around for centuries without deteriorating. The pearmain apple has been cultivated for more than 700 years and the Rein Claude pear for more than 400 years. Some plant cells can be maintained for long periods in tissue culture without loss of vigor (although a slow but steady decline in vigor is more common).

Senescence occurs in several patterns which indicates that it is a controlled phenomenon based on genetics. In monocarpic species the whole plant senesces, timed to the end of the flowering and seed production processes. In the spring bulbs and others there is *top senescence* in which all the above ground parts are lost and the in-ground part goes dormant until it produces a complete new set of above ground parts the next year. In *deciduous senescence* all the leaves die but the stems and roots stay intact. In *progressive senescence* the oldest leaves are lost as they are replaced by new ones.

Stress resulting from the temperature or from deficiencies of nutrients, water, or light may lead to senescence but the unusual pattern of the oldest structures being the first to go still holds. In these cases the controlled loss of body parts can easily be recognized as adaptive responses.

An inevitable question is whether the plant dies because of changes made by its cells without a central decision or if the cells die because of the throwing of some master switch in one part of the plant. Is whole plant senescence a cellular or an organismic phenomenon? The fact that vigorous new plants can be produced by asexual culturing of cells from senescent plants suggests that the position of the cell within the plant is most important but since ultimately all events in any living thing result from cellular activities even though influenced by the environment it is not possible to get a clear cut answer to this chicken or egg type question.

Whole plant senescence is preceded or accompanied by a decrease or even total cessation of shoot and root growth. There is usually a somewhat similar reduction in vegetative growth during the reproductive phase so that the available resources can be focused on flower and seed production although in some species like the morning glory (*Ipomea caerulea*) vigorous vegetative growth continues during flowering. In many species removing the flowers after they have opened but before they have matured any seed will hold off the cessations of growth or the onset of senescence but in the cocklebur *Xanthium strumarium* once they have formed the plant is doomed no matter what happens to the flowers. Cessation of stem growth is often a sign of senescence but decapitation studies (what is it with these botanists?!) find that in most species it is not the *cause* of the senescence – yet again with a full list of variations and exceptions.

The flower structures may do more that just hog all the resources though. In some cases they set off an irreversible chain of physiological events that leads directly to the death of that plant. Such monocarpic or "one batch of seed" species include some bamboos and palms, and many bromeliads.

Not enough study has been done on polycarpic species to make generalizations but in well studied monocarpic types it is usually the flower-fruit, and especially the seeds developing within it, that cause the whole plant senescence. Many degenerative changes occur and a decline in one body part, especially the decline in photosynthesis and the abscission of leaves, begins to affect other parts. There are complicated and not yet entirely unraveled hormonal interactions involved.

There are several theories to explain why the whole plant senesces after flowering in monocarpic species. One suggests that these species simply have a genetically limited longevity or growth potential and they have worn themselves out by the time they mature enough to make their one round of flowers. They do not have mechanisms to allow them to rebuild their resources so they die of exhaustion and leave the race to their offspring.

A second theory says that the developing fruit drains off so much of one or more specific nutrient like nitrogen that the other tissues die of a deficiency of that material that is in limited supply. In theory then these plants would not die if the supply of just those particular heavy demand nutrients were available but they seldom are. A third theory maintains that it is not any particular nutrient that is in critically limited supply but all the energy storage and cell repair materials. This theory says that the parent plant starves to death while nurturing the offspring. In this case it is the general supply of stored nutrients that is deficient, not any particular category.

A fourth theory goes the positive route and suggests that it is the synthesis of specific senescence hormones, not a deficiency of anything, that triggers the response. This theory seems to leave room for so far undetected additional hormones or for some undeciphered shift in the balance between the ones we know of to do the job.

Leaf senescence has been widely studied both because of its importance and because of its convenience since it can be induced when it is convenient for the researchers. There are a predictable set of changes and they may occur more or less simultaneously or in sequence if we are watching closely enough. Leaves can vary the order and extent of the loss of their components just as whole plants can senescence some parts but not others – like dropping the flower petals but retaining the ovary. In functional phloem sieve cells, for instance, the ER, tonoplast, ribosomes, and nucleus break down but not the plastids, mitochondria, or plasma membrane.

The first change we can notice in the intact plant is a loss of chlorophyll. The enzymatic digestion of various molecule types and structures is readily detected by chemical analysis. There is a reduction in the RNA content of the cells as they shutdown protein synthesis. At the start of the sequence when the various digestive enzymes are being made and other processes begun there is a sharp rise in the rate of cellular respiration to supply the needed energy. That is followed later by a sharp drop in the respiration rate as everything winds down. Microscopic examination of the cells will also reveal the various plastids degenerating, the number of cristae folds within the mitochondria being reduced, and the free ribosomes disappearing since they are no longer needed in a cell doing no protein synthesis. Fall leaf color is characteristic of senescence but as far as we can see has no advantage for the plant, it is merely a side effect of senescence that does no harm so it is not counteracted.

Sometimes senescence is reversible. If lower leaves on a stem are gradually being shaded by the enlargement of new ones higher up they begin to lose more and more of their chloroplasts but if an herbivore or something else removes the shading leaves the lower ones that have not degenerated too far will often recover their full photosynthetic capacity.

In evergreens the senescent of old leaves is delayed until a new set are established. This permits the direct transfer of many organic molecules from the old to the new. Some of the minerals are also transferred directly rather than depending on the slower and less certain recycling route by way of the soil microbes.

Evergreen seedlings must grow for long periods in the shade of the mature trees and one of their adaptations is to conserve their resources by reducing their respiration to a low rate during low light periods. H.W. Woolhouse describes an experiment of punching pieces from evergreen leaves and floating them on water in the dark at room temperature along with pieces from leaves of the cereal grains. A month later the pieces of evergreen leaf are likely to still be green and healthy although the other pieces died within three or four days.

Some species routinely produce more flowers that they can support as fruit and then abort or absciss the excess when it is clear how many of them they will actually be able to open and how many get pollinated, both variables of consequence to the plant. Since the flower buds of many woody plants like cherries start to form the summer before they will be used it is a safer strategy to produce many and drop those not actually needed because there is no way to recover a full year of breeding potential if the first blossoms fail due to a storm or a freeze at the wrong time that destroys them or poor pollinator turnout that leaves many of them sterile. This overproduction followed by thinning does not seem to correlate with senescence but it is unclear whether the plant uses the same mechanism for both vegetative and fruit senescence.

BIBLIOGRAPHY

BOOKS

Abscission, Fredrick Addicott, Univ. Calif Press, 1982
Adaptive Geometry of Trees, The, Henry Horn, Monographs in Population Biology #3, Princeton Univ Press, 1971
All About Weeds, Edwin Rollin Spencer, Dover Books, 1940
Allelopathy, E. Rice, Academic Press, 1974
Amazing Seeds, The, Ross Hutchins, Dodd, Mead, 1960
Anatomy of Flowering Plants, Paula Rudall, Cambridge Univ. Press, 1992
Art of Shaping Shrubs, Trees and Other Plants, The, T. & K. Ishimoto, Crown, 1966
Art of Training Plants, The, Ernesta Drinker Ballard, Harper & Row, 1962
Atlas of Plant Life, Herbert Edlin, John Day Publications, 1973
Bark: The Formation, Characteristics and Uses of Bark Around the World, Ghillian Tolmie Prance and Anne E. Prance, Timber Press, 1993
Beginner's Guide to Botany, C.L. Duddington, Drake Publications, 1970
Biography of a Tree, The, James Jackson, Jonathan David Publications, 1979
Biology, L.G. Johnson, Wm. C. Brown Col., 1983
Biology: Life on Earth, G. & T. Audesiak, Macmillan, 1986
Biology of Nectaries, The, ed by Barbara Bentley & Thomas Elia, Columbia Univ Press, 1983
Biology of Plants, 3rd edit. Raven, Evert & Curtis, Worth Publications, 1981
Biology of Vines, The, ed. by F.E. Putz & H.A. Mooney, Cambridge Univ Press, 1992
Blue Corn and Square Tomatoes, R. Rupp, Garden Way Publications, 1987
Book About Grass, A, Mary Hunt Kaglenburg & Mark Schwartz, Dutton, 1983
Botanical Latin, 3rd edition, Wm Stearn, David & Charles, 1983

Botanical World, The, Northington & Goodin, Mosby, 1984
Botany: A Human Concern, Rayle & Wedberg, Houghton Mifflin, 1975
Botany: An Introduction to Plant Biology, James Mauseth, Saunders, 1991
Botany for Gardeners, H.W. Rickett, Macmillan, 1957
Botany: Principles and Applications, R. & B. Saigo, Prentice Hall, 1983
Cell Biology: A Molecular Approach, R.D. Dyson, Allay & Bacon, 1974
Cells and Organelles, 3rd edit., E. Holtzmann & A.B. Novikoff, Saunders, 1984
Climate and Plant Distribution, F.I. Woodward, Cambridge Univ Press, 1987
Climate, Soils and Vegetation, D.C. Money, Univ. Toronto Press, 1965
Color in Plants and Flowers, J. & S. Proctor, Everest House, 1978
Commercial Floriculture, Fritz Bahr, A.T. DeLaMare Col., 1922
Commercia Flower Forcing, 7th edit., Laurie, Kiplinger & Nelson, McGraw-Hill, 1969
Common Weeds of the United States, USDA, Dover Books, 1971
Control of Growth and Differentiation in Plants, The, P.F. Wareing & I.D.J. Phillips, Pergamon Press, 1970
Create New Flowers and Plants, John James, Doubleday, 1964
Curiosities of the Plant Kingdom, Reinhardt Hohn, Universe Books, 1980
Cytoplasmic Genes and Organelles, R. Sager, Academic Press, 1973
Dangerous Plants, J. Tampion, Universe Books, 1977
Darwin and His Flowers: The Key To Natural Selection, Mea Allen, Taplinger, 1977
Development and Function of Roots, The, ed. by J.G. Torrey & D.T. Clarkson, Academic Press, 1975
Diseases and Pests of Ornamental Plants, 4th edit., Pascal Pirone, Ronald Press, 1970
Earthly Pleasures: Tales from a Biologist's Garden, Roger Swain, Penguin, 1981
Evergreen Form Studies, G. Robinette, Van Nostrand Reinhold, 1983
Evolution of Plants and Flowers, The, Barry Thomas, St. Martin's Press, 1981
Families of Flowering Plants, Richard Headstrom, Barnes, 1978
Fantastic Trees: Marvels and Monstrosities of the Arboreal World, Edwin Menninger, Viking Books, 1967
Features of Evolution in the Flowering Plants, Ronald Good, Dover Books, 1974
Field Days: Journal of an Itinerant Biologist, Roger Swain, Penguin, 1983

Flower and Vegetable Plant Breeding, Leslie Watts, Grower Books, London 1980

Flowering Plants: Evolution Above The Species Level, G. Ledyard Stebbins, Harvard Univ Press, 1974

Forest Killers, The: The Destruction of the American Wildnerness, Jack Shepard, Weybright & Talley, 1975

Fragrant Gardens, Jane Taylor, Salem House, 1987

Genetic Improvement of Crops: Emergent Techniques: Rubenstein, Gengenbach, Phillips & Green, Univ. Minnesota Press, 1980

Genetics of Flowering Plants, Verne Grant, Columbia Univ Press, 1975

Germination of Seeds, The, 4th edit, A.N. Mayer & A. Poljokoff-Mayber, Pergamon Press, 1989

Grass: The Everything, Everywhere Plant, Augusta Goldin, Thos. Nelson Publications, 1977

Gray's New Manual of Botany, 7th edit., revised and rearranged by L. Robinson & M.L. Fernald; American Book Co., 1908

Green Inheritance, Anthony Huxley, Doubleday, 1985

Green Medicine: The Search for Plants That Heal, Margaret Kreig, Rand-McNally, 1964

Green Planet: The Story of Plant Life on Earth, ed. by D. Moore, Cambridge Univ Press, 1982

Green Wisdom, Arthur W. Galston, Perigee Books, 1981

Green World, The: An Introduction to Plants and People, Richard Klein, Harper and Row, 1979

Groundwork: A Gardener's Ecology, Roger Swain, Houghton, Mifflin, 1994

Growing Fragrant Plants, R.C. Reddell & R. Galyean, Harper & Row, 1989

Handbook of Experimental Pollination Biology, ed. by C.E. Jones and R.J. Littley, Van Nostrand Reinhold, 1983

Heterosis, ed. by J.W. Gowen, Hafner Publications, 1964.

How Flowers Work, R. Gibbons, Blandford Publications, 1984

How Indians Use Wild Plants for Food, Medicine and Crafts, Frances Densmore, Dover Books, 1928

How Plants Get Their Names, L.H. Bailey, Dover Books, 1963

Humanistic Botany, Tippo & Stern, W.W. Norton Co., 1977

In Harmony with Wood, C. Becksvoort, Van Nostrand Reinhold, 1983

Incredible Plants: Oddities, Curiosities and Eccentricities, Robert Lee Behme, Sterling, 1992

Ingenious Kingdom: The Remarkable World of Plants; H. & R. Northen, Prentice-Hall, 1970
Inside Wood: Masterpiece of Nature, W. Harlow, Amer. Forestry Assoc., 1970
International Book of Trees, The, Hugh Johnson, Bonanza Books, 1973
International Book of Wood, The: Edited by M. Bramwell, Crescent Books, 1987
Introduction to Plant Cell Development, An, Jeremy Burgess, Cambridge Univ Press, 1985
Introduction to Plant Physiology, Meyer, Anderson, Bohning & Frattianne, 2nd edit., Van Nostrand Reinhold, 1973
Introduction to Plant Taxonomy, An, George H.M. Lawrence, Macmillan, 1955
Introductory Botany, 2nd edit., Arthur Cronquist, Harper & Row, 1971
Landmarks of Botanical History, 2 vols, Edward Lee Greene, Stanford Univ Press., 1983
Leaves, G.T. Prance, Crown, 1985
Life of Plants, The, E.J.H. Corner, World Publications Co., 1963
Life: The Science of Biology, W.K. Purves & C.H. Orians, Willard Grant Press, 1983
Long-Shadowed Forest, The, Helen Hoover, W.W. Norton, 1963
Looking at Plants, David Suzuki, Warner Books, 1985
Mate Choice in Plants, Mary Willson & Nancy Burley, Monographs in Population Biology #19, Princeton Univ Press, 1983
Miniature Rose Book, The, Margaret E. Pinney, Van Nostrand Reinhold, 1964
Modern Plant Biology, Howard Dittmer, Van Nostrand Reinhold, 1972
Molecular Plant Development, T. Murphy & W. Thompson, Prentice-Hall, 1988
Morphogenesis in Plants, C.W. Wardlaw, Metheum, 1968
Nature: Mother of Invention, Felix Paturi, Harper & Row, 1976
Nature of Plants, The, Lorus & Margery Milne, Lippincott, 1971
New Plants from Old: Pruning and Propagating for the Indoor Gardener, Charles Evans, Random House, 1976
New Tree Biology, A, Alex L. Shigo, Shigo and Trees Assoc., 1986
Organelles, M. Carroll, Guilford Press, 1989
Organogenesis of Flowers: A Photographic Text-Atlas, Rolf Sattler, Univ Toronto, 1973

Origin of Cultivated Plants, The, F. Schwanitz, Harvard Univ Press, 1967
Our Flowering World, Rutherford Platt, Dodd, Mead, 1947
Our Green and Living World: The Wisdom to Save It, Ayensu, Heywood, Lucas & DeFillips, Smithsonian Institution Press, 1984
Penguin Dictionary of Botany, Allen Lane Publications, 1984
Peter Malins' Rose Book, Peter Malins and M.M. Graf, Dodd, Mead, 1979
Photoperiodism in Plants, D. Vince-Prue, McGraw-Hill, 1975
Pigments in Vegetables: Chlorophylls and Carotenoids, Jeana Gross, Van Nostrand Reinhold, 1991
Pioneers of Plant Study, Ellison Hawks, Books for Libraries Press, 1928
Plant Anatomy, A. Fahn, 4rd edit, Pergamon Press, 1990
Plant and Planet, Anthony Huxley, Viking, 1974
Plant Breeding Systems, A.J. Richards, George Allen & Unwin Publications, 1986
Plant Classification, Lyman Benson, D.C. Heath & Co., 1957
Plant Form and Function, Tortora, Cicero and Parish, Macmillan, 1970
Plant Genetic Engineering, Vol 1, ed. by Don Grierson, Blackie & Son Ltd., 1991
Plant Hormones and Plant Development, Wm. Jacobs, Cambridge Univ Press, 1979
Plant Life: Readings from Scientific American, Simon & Schuster, 1957
Plant Kingdom, The, 4th edit., Harold Bold, Prentice-Hall Foundations in Modern Biology Series, 1977
Plant Kingdom, The, Ian Tribe, Grosset & Dunlap, 1970
Plant Observer's Guidebook, The: Field Botany Manual, Charles Roth, Prentice-Hall, 1984
Plant Physiology, R.G.S. Bidwell, Macmillan, 1974
Plant Propagaion, Principles and Practices, 3rd edit., Hudson Hartmann & Dale Kester, Prentice-Hall, 1975
Plant Science: An Introduction to World Crops, Janick, Schery, Woods and Ruttan, W.H. Freeman Co., 1969
Plant Speciation, Verne Grant, Columbia Univ Press, 1971
Plant Tropisms and Other Growth Movements, James W. Hart, Unwin Hyman, 1990
Plant World, The, Jean Vallin, Sterling Publications, 1969
Plants and Environment: A Textbook of Plant Autecology, 2nd edit., R.F. Daubenmire, Wiley, 1959

Plants in Action, A. Hibbert & J. Brooks, BBC Books, 1981
Plants, Man and the Ecosystem, 2nd edit., W.D. Billings, Fundamentals of Botany Series, Wadsworth, 1970
Plants, Man and Life, Edgar Anderson, Univ Calif Press, 1952
Plants That Changed the World, Bertha S. Dodge, Little, Brown & Co., 1959
Plants That Feed The World, R. Frisch, Van Nostrand Reinhold, 1966
Plantwatching, Malcolm Wilkins, Facts On File Publications, 1988
Pollen: Biology, Biochemistry, Management, R.G. Stanley & H.F. Lenskens, Springer-Verlag, 1974
Pollination Biology, ed. by Leslie Real, Academic Press, 1983
Power of Plants, The, Brendan Lehane, McGraw-Hill, 1977
Principles of Cell Biology, L.J. Kleinsmith & V.M. Kish, Harper Collins, 1995
Principles of Dispersal in Higher Plants, 2nd edit., L. van der Pyl, Springer-Verlag, 1972
Principles of Pollination Ecology, The, 3rd edit., K. Faaegri & L. van der Pijl, Pergamon Press, 1979
Private Lives of Plants, The, David Attenborough, Princeton Univ Press, 1995
Production of Field Crops: A Textbook of Agronomy, 6th edit., M.S. Kipps, McGraw-Hill, 1970
Rhythmic Phenomena in Plants, B.M. Sweeney, Academic Press, 1969
Roots: Miracles Below, C.M. Wilson, Doubleday, 1968
Scent in Your Garden, S. Lacey, Little, Brown & Co., 1991
Scented Flora of the World, Roy Genders, St. Martin's Press, 1977
Scented Garden, The, R. Verey, Van Nostrand Reinhold, 1981
Secret Life of Plants, The, Peter Tompkins and Christopher Bird, Harper & Row, 1973
Secrets of Companion Planting for Successful Gardening, Louise Riote, Garden Way, 1975
Seed Germination Theory and Practice, 2nd edit., Norman C. Deno, Private publication, State College, PA, 1993
Seeds of Change: Five Plants that Transformed Mankind, Henry Hobhouse, Harper & Row, 1985
Seeds of Change: 500 Years Since Columbus, H. Viola & C. Margolis, Smithsonian Institution Press, 1991
Seeds of Change: The Living Treasure, K. Ausubel, Harper, 1994

Seeds: Physiology of Development and Germination, J.D. Bewley & M. Black, Plenum, 1984
Senescence in Plants, ed. by K.T. Thiman, CRC Press, 1980
Sex Life of Flowers, The, B. Meeuse & S. Morris, Facts on File Publications, 1984
Sex Life of Plants, The, Alex Bristow, Holt, Rinehart & Winston, 1978
Study of Plant Communities, The, Henry Oosting, Freeman, 1953
This Green World, Rutherford Platt, Dodd, Mead, 1949
Three-Dimensionatl Structure of Wood, 2nd edit., B.G. Butterfield & B.A. Meylan, Chapman & Hall, 1980
Trees, Andreas Feininger, Viking Books, 1968
Trees and Man, Herbert Edlin, Columbia Univ Press, 1976
Underground Plant Life: A Guide to Root Varieties, Structures and Growth, Charles Self, Drake Publications, 1978
Uniqueness of the Individual, The, Medawar, P.B., Metheun, London 1957 (reprints "An unsolved problem of Biology", 1952)
Untamed Garden and Other Personal Essays, The, David Rains Wallace, Ohio State Univ Press, 1986
Various Contrivances by Which Orchids are Fertilized by Insects, The, Charles Darwin, Univ Chicago Press, 1877/1984
Virology of Flowering Plants, W.A. Stevens, Chapman & Hall, 1983
Weeds, 2nd edit., Walter Conrad Muenscher, Cornell Univ. Press, 1980
Weeds and Words: Entymology of Scientific Names of Weeds and Crops, Robert Zimdahl, Iowa State Univ Press, 1989
Who Named the Daisy? Who Named the Rose?: A Roving Dictionary of North American Wild Flowers, Mary Durant, Dodd, Mead, 1976
Why Does Your Garden Grow? The Facts of Plant Life, W. Van Dersal, Quadrangle Books, 1977
Wildly Successful Plants: Handbook of North American Weeds, L. Crockett, Collier Books, 1977
Winter Botany: An Identification Guide of Native Trees and Shrubs, 3rd edit., W. Trelease, Dover Books, 1931
World Vegetation Types, ed. by S.R. Eyre, Columbia Univ. Press, 1971
World Without Trees, Robert Lamb, Paddington Press, 1979

ARTICLES

"ABCs of Floral Homeotic Genes, The", Detly Weigel and Elliot M. Meyerowitz, *Cell* 78: 203-209 (July 1994)

"Cell's Nucleus Shapes Up, The," M. Hoffman, *Science* 259:1257-59, 26 Feb. 1993

"Chimaeras," P.J.S. Cramer, *Bibliographica Genetica*, XVI: 193-381, 1954

"Control of Plant Growth, The," J. van Overbeek, *Sci Amer* 219, #1, pp. 75-81 (July 1968)

"For Your Own Good" (Bees and parasites), *Discover* Aug 1995

"Garden of Mutants, A" (*Arabidopsis* Floral Genes), C. Fletcher, *Discover*, Aug. 1995

"Genetic Engineering Turns to Trees," A.S. Moffat, *Science* 271:761, 9 Feb 1996

"Individual and Population Shifts in Flower Color by Scarlet Gilia," *Science* 227:315, 18 Jan 1985

"Is That a Pistil In Your Pocket?" R. Mestel, *Discover*, Jan 1995

"Leaf Shelters are Mite-y Amenities," *Sci News* Jan 30, 1988

"Lectins as Cell Recognition Molecules," N. Sharon & H. Lis, *Science* 246:227-34, 13 Oct 1989

"Monkeyflowers: A Leap for Nature," T. Adler, *Sci News* 148:148 Sept 2, 1995

"No Genome Barriers to Promiscuous DNA," R. Lewin, *Science* 224:970-71, 1 June 1984

"Of Bedouins, Beetles and Blooms," B. Henrich, *Nat Hist*, May 1994

"Pigment Distribution, Light Reflection and Cell Structure in Petals," Ky et al, *Bot J Linnaean Soc* 83:57-84 (1988)

"Plant Embryogenesis: Zygote to Seed," R.B. Goldberg *et al.*, *Science* 266:605-13, 28 Oct 1994

"Plant Growth Regulators," L.G. Nickel, *Chem & Engin.*, Oct 9, 1978

"Plant Parenthood and the Single Cell," R. Adams II, *Horticulture*, Oct 1978

"Plasmodesmata: Plant Channels for Molecules on the Move," P. Zambryski, *Science* 270:1943-44, 22 Dec 1995

"Pollen Shortcomings," N.M. Waser, *Nat Hist*, July 1984

"Relax and Expand," Discover, March 1995

"Relaxed Cellular Controls and Organelle Heredity," C.W. Birky Jr. *Science* 222:468-75, 4 Nov 1983

"Secrets of a Cryptic Flower," D. Wiens, *Nat Hist*, Nov 1983

"Senescence processes in the life cycle of flowering plants," H.W. Woolhouse, *Bioscience* 28:25-31 (1978)

"Sex and the Single Flower," P.A. Cox, *Nat Hist*, Nov. 1983

"Sex Determination Process in Maize, The," S.L. Dellaporta & A. Calderon-Urrea, *Science* 266:1501-05, 2 Dec 1994

"Sexual Dimorphism in *Catasetum* Orchids," G.A. Romero & C.E. Nelson, *Science* 232:1538-40, 20 June 1986

"Smell of Success, The," C. Galen, *Nat Hist*, July 1985

"Something to Chew On," K. Leutwyler, *Sci Amer*, June 1994

"Variation Among Floral Visitors in Pollination Ability," D.W. Schemske & C.C. Horwitz, *Science* 225:519-21, 3 Aug 1984

"Water-Pollinated Plants," P.A. Cox, *Sci Amer*, Oct 1993

"Waves in the Forest," P.J. Marchard, *Nat Hist* Feb 1995

"With Single Cells, Instead of Whole Plants, Scientists Use Genetic Engineering to Breed New Super Plants," E. Driscoll, *Horticulture*, Feb 1978

INDEX

abscission, 6, 132, 135, 136, 137, 138, 139, 140, 145, 146, 149, 150, 190, 194
absorption, 38, 99, 154, 158
amino acids, 22, 51, 59, 60, 61, 87, 138
Angiosperms, 185
anthers, 79, 140, 178
antibodies, 21, 53
apomixis, 71
bark, 11, 114, 117, 137, 140, 168
branches, 12, 13, 14, 17, 129, 132, 133, 137, 177, 187
branching, 132
buds, 12, 14, 130, 131, 132, 137, 140, 145, 147, 148, 149, 151, 156, 196
calyx, 186
cambium, 25, 117, 145, 147
cell division, 10, 11, 14, 17, 23, 25, 34, 41, 56, 61, 64, 68, 86, 88, 89, 98, 113, 127, 130, 145, 148, 172
cell elongation, 33
cell wall, 10, 11, 15, 16, 27, 28, 29, 31, 32, 33, 34, 35, 38, 45, 104, 106, 108, 112, 113, 114, 115, 116, 117, 125, 127, 128, 137, 140, 145, 147, 158, 159, 171
cell walls, 10, 11, 15, 27, 28, 29, 31, 32, 33, 34, 35, 38, 45, 112, 114, 115, 116, 117, 125, 128, 137, 140, 145, 147, 171
cellular parts, 19
cellular respiration, 83, 95, 97, 195
cellular structure, 19
cellulose, 29, 30, 31, 32, 33, 34, 113, 114, 115, 116, 147
Cellulose, 29, 31
Charles Darwin, 175, 203
chlorophyll, 93, 94, 95, 96, 97, 99, 100, 114, 155, 159, 164, 191, 195
chloroplasts, 10, 34, 63, 88, 93, 94, 95, 96, 97, 98, 100, 101, 104, 114, 115, 155, 158, 159, 196
cholesterol, 40, 41, 86, 97, 105
chromosome, 11, 59, 70, 80, 130
chromosomes, 17, 58, 60, 61, 68, 69, 70, 71, 87, 89
circumnutation, 177
cork, 11, 27, 32, 117, 131
cortex, 112, 114
cuticle, 32
Cyanobacteria, 1
cytoplasm, 11, 21, 35, 38, 39, 41, 42, 48, 49, 52, 56, 57, 59, 60, 83, 87,

89, 94, 104, 105, 108, 109, 128, 158
Cytoskeleton, 41, 52, 53
dead cells, 11, 16, 116, 178
deciduous, 16, 139, 168, 187, 193
differentiation, 127, 130, 146, 147
diffusion, 44
diploid, 17, 119, 126, 130
DNA, 17, 48, 55, 56, 57, 58, 59, 60, 61, 63, 68, 69, 70, 80, 86, 87, 88, 89, 90, 91, 95, 98, 99, 100, 107, 130, 147, 193, 204
dormancy, 6, 16, 139, 148, 149, 175, 189, 190, 191
embryo, 98, 107, 124, 189
embryonic, 11, 14, 17, 112, 129, 189
endosperm, 71, 107
Enzymes, 22, 28, 30, 33, 42, 50, 53, 54, 59, 60, 86, 97, 105, 106, 107, 108, 136, 138, 195
epidermis, 112, 114, 115, 158, 160
ER, v, 47, 49, 50, 52, 56, 103, 104, 105, 106, 108, 195
eucaryotic cell, 1, 38, 39, 49, 51, 55, 56, 58, 59, 60, 87, 88, 105, 108
evaporation, 163
fertilization, 17, 24, 25, 68, 71, 189
fertilizer, 80
filament, 56
flowering, 7, 10, 11, 19, 90, 95, 117, 120, 122, 124, 130, 131, 135, 136, 145, 148, 149, 150, 155, 156, 158, 175, 182, 184, 185, 186, 187, 189, 193, 194, 205
Flowering, 87, 197, 198, 199, 201, 203
fruit, 12, 17, 78, 96, 120, 121, 136, 138, 139, 140, 141, 145, 146, 148, 150, 154, 184, 186, 187, 195, 196
gametophytes, 56
genes, 17, 21, 22, 43, 52, 56, 57, 58, 60, 61, 63, 64, 67, 68, 69, 70, 71, 74, 76, 77, 78, 79, 80, 87, 88, 89, 90, 91, 95, 98, 119, 120, 122, 125, 126, 128, 138, 160, 161, 190, 192
genomes, 59, 86, 88, 89, 90, 193
germinate, 124
germination, 76, 107, 123, 148, 158, 175, 189
Germination, 199, 202, 203
glucose, 29, 30, 94, 95, 99, 107
grafting, 123
gravitropism, 104, 173, 174
growing season, 13, 17, 124, 129, 132, 137, 139
haploid, 17, 126
hormone, 138, 143, 144, 145, 147, 148, 149, 150, 151, 157, 172, 173, 174
hormones, ix, 2, 34, 42, 137, 138, 139, 143, 144, 145, 149, 151, 173, 195
hybrids, 17, 74, 75, 76, 77, 78, 79, 80, 98, 123, 126, 145, 164, 165, 181
hypocotyl, 158
internodes, 118
irritability, 10, 171
laticifers, 112
leaves, 7, 12, 13, 14, 15, 16, 21, 27, 32, 33, 38, 42, 89, 94, 101, 109, 114, 115, 122, 129, 131, 132, 134, 135, 136, 137, 138, 139, 140, 145,

146, 148, 149, 150, 155, 158, 159, 161, 162, 163, 164, 165, 167, 168, 171, 172, 177, 178, 179, 181, 184, 186, 193, 194, 196
life cycles, 189
Lignins, 32, 35, 115
Lipid, 37, 39, 40, 41, 42, 43, 50, 52, 56, 96, 97, 101, 106, 107, 164
living cell, 19, 27, 48, 83, 85, 156
lumber, 29
macrofibrils, 29
magnesium, 22, 31, 32
meiosis, 17, 25, 68, 69, 70, 71, 98
membrane barriers, 34
membranes, v, 37, 38, 39, 45, 96
meristem, 13, 55, 112, 114, 116, 117, 118, 122, 129, 130, 148
microfibrils, 29
mineral nutrients, 1, 133
mitosis, 11, 88, 98, 115, 116, 118
molecules, 2, 10, 22, 23, 25, 26, 28, 29, 30, 32, 34, 38, 39, 40, 41, 42, 43, 45, 50, 51, 52, 53, 55, 56, 57, 59, 60, 61, 63, 83, 84, 85, 86, 87, 89, 93, 94, 95, 96, 97, 99, 100, 101, 104, 105, 106, 107, 116, 119, 128, 129, 131, 138, 139, 143, 144, 146, 147, 151, 153, 154, 155, 156, 159, 164, 174, 190, 192, 196
multicellular, 1, 6, 9, 11, 17, 20, 22, 23, 25, 26, 30, 58, 64, 68, 111, 119, 143, 189
Muscles, 27, 111
nectar, 8, 63, 166, 192
nitrogen, 22, 80, 101, 138, 157, 195
node, 187
nucleii, 125

odors, 161, 162, 164, 167
Offspring, 12, 15, 17, 66, 69, 70, 73, 74, 76, 78, 120, 125, 190, 192, 193, 195
Organelles, 20, 21, 34, 38, 39, 48, 52, 55, 57, 83, 85, 87, 88, 89, 90, 94, 98, 103, 104, 105, 107, 108, 128, 191, 192
ornamentals, 78, 147
osmosis, 16, 29, 41, 45
ovary, 186, 195
ovule, 124
Pectin, 27, 31, 32, 111, 113, 114
pericycle, 112, 114
petiole, 136, 138, 172, 176, 186
phloem, 11, 112, 117, 147, 195
phospholipid, 39, 40, 41, 42, 86, 97
photomorphogenesis, 175
photoperiod, 156
photoperiodism, 151, 157, 175
photosynthesis, 1, 12, 21, 25, 27, 30, 64, 93, 97, 99, 100, 101, 104, 107, 114, 116, 117, 128, 131, 133, 138, 139, 154, 156, 159, 175, 189, 194
phototropism, 104, 173, 175, 176
pistil, 79, 182
pistils, 186
pith, 114
plant body, vii, ix, 6, 16, 43, 44, 112, 114, 116, 135, 136, 146, 184
plant growth, 10, 14, 120, 127, 128, 129, 145, 175
plasma membrane, 32, 34, 38, 41, 42, 43, 44, 45, 50, 52, 103, 104, 105, 106, 195
plasma membranes, 41, 42, 45
plasmodesmata, 34

Plasmodesmata, 33, 204
plasmolysis, 42
pollen, 17, 28, 34, 67, 68, 71, 78, 79, 80, 125, 126, 141, 145, 166, 172, 177, 178
pollination, 12, 79, 80, 124, 140, 146, 166, 171
pollinators, 162
Polysaccharide, 16, 29, 30
Protein, 2, 11, 21, 22, 25, 32, 34, 37, 39, 40, 41, 43, 44, 45, 51, 52, 53, 57, 58, 59, 60, 61, 68, 74, 80, 85, 86, 87, 96, 97, 106, 107, 148, 157, 195
protoplasm, 10, 12, 20, 22, 25, 27, 33, 34, 50, 125, 127, 128, 131
protoplast, 42
pruning, 193
R. canina inermis, 7
receptacle, 186, 187
reproduction, 1, 14, 17, 64, 71, 77, 89, 119, 120, 121, 122, 182, 184
resins, 168
ribosomes, 50, 51, 52, 56, 57, 59, 60, 86, 87, 88, 99, 100, 106, 195
RNA, 51, 55, 58, 60, 61, 84, 88, 147, 192, 195
root cap, 106, 174
rotenone, 2
rubber, 49, 104
scents, 161, 162, 163, 165, 167, 168, 169
secondary growth, 190
seed, 6, 7, 12, 65, 66, 67, 71, 74, 78, 79, 80, 116, 120, 123, 124, 125, 129, 140, 146, 148, 166, 173, 184, 185, 189, 190, 191, 193, 194

seed coat, 66, 67, 116, 124
seed dispersal, 140
seed production, 120, 148, 191, 193, 194
self-pollinating, 79
self-shading, 15
senescence, 6, 137, 138, 148, 190, 191, 193, 194, 195, 196
sepals, 159, 163, 182, 186, 187
shoot, 3, 13, 14, 114, 120, 129, 130, 132, 140, 146, 147, 148, 174, 175, 176, 177, 185, 190, 194
shrubs, 167, 186, 190
soil, 2, 13, 14, 15, 109, 122, 124, 133, 138, 139, 140, 145, 167, 173, 174, 178, 185, 189, 190, 196
specialization, 1, 23, 26, 113, 127
spores, 178
stamens, 164, 172, 177, 182, 186
starch, 16, 30, 96, 99, 174
stems, 4, 7, 12, 13, 14, 17, 27, 32, 33, 94, 114, 115, 116, 118, 122, 129, 130, 131, 146, 147, 148, 159, 163, 167, 168, 171, 173, 174, 175, 185, 187, 193
sterile, 17, 77, 78, 196
sterility, 78
stomate, 177
sunlight, 12, 15, 117, 153, 157, 185
tannins, 32
taxonomic names, 179, 180, 182, 183
transcription, 57
transport process, 43
trees, 2, 12, 14, 17, 28, 80, 81, 132, 133, 134, 136, 140, 173, 190, 196
tropism mechanisms, 177
ultraviolet, 153

understock, 7
UV radiation, 154
vacuole, 10, 11, 35, 103, 104, 108, 115, 158
vacuoles, 103, 104, 108, 114
vegetation, 133
water absorption, 173
wood, viii, 6, 31, 33, 35, 49, 80, 115, 116, 133, 158, 168
Wood, 199, 200, 203
woody tissue, 12, 114, 133
xylem, 11, 108, 112, 113, 115, 116, 117, 147
Xylem, 116
zygote, 23, 64, 98